IF IT GLITTERS

THE STORY OF THE METAL KNOWN AS GOLD

BY

ROBERT R. BAREFOOT

IF IT GLITTERS
The Story of the Metal Known As Gold
By
Robert R. Barefoot
Published By
Pan American International Nutrition Ltd. Publishing
P.O. Box 21389
Wickenburg, AZ 85358

Copyright © 2008 by Robert R. Barefoot,
First Printing November 1999, Second Printing June 2008.
Printed in the United States of America.

Library of Congress Cataloging in Publication Data
Barefoot, Robert R.
If It Glitters, The Story of the Metal Known as Gold
            by Robert R. Barefoot --- 1st edition
Bibliography
Includes Subjects:

1. How Much Gold is There on Earth
2. In the Beginning, Man's First Encounter With Gold
3. Gold and Christopher Columbus
4. Gold in the New World
5. The World's First Gold Recovery Process, The Patio Process
6. The Cyanide Process and Clay Interference
7. The Creation of New Wealth By Gold
8. Platinum Scams
9. Gold Scam
10. A New Approach to the Recovery of Invisible Gold
11. Development and Failure to Exploit the Differential Charge Recovery
12. The Recovery of Unassayable Invisible Gold, the World's Largest Deposit
13. Massive Gold Deposits in Porphyry Copper

Library of Congress Catalog Card Number, C.I.P. 99-094758
ISBN 978-0-9633703-4-1
Printed in the United States

Order Form
Web Site: "barefootscureamerica.com"

Name: _____

Address: _____

_____

_____

Phone Number: _____

Country/Zip: _____

Yes, I / We would like to order more copies of **If It Glitters!**
or the following other books by the author   **The Calcium Factor**
                     or   **Death By Diet**

     Please send ____copies of @ $24.95 US each ($25.00 Canadian)
                           for a total of $ _____

     Of the following books _____

                     _____

                     _____

     Please allow a shipping and handling charge of $5.00 US
               ($7.00 Canadian) per book: $ _____
     Arizona residents please add appropriate tax: $ _____

                   Total Enclosed: $ _____

(Please check addition carefully; incorrect totals will be returned unfulfilled.)

     Please allow 2 to 6 weeks for delivery.
     A quantity discount schedule is available on request.

Mail this order form (or a copy) along with a check for the total amount
to:
Pan American International Nutrition Ltd.
P.O. Box 21389
Wickenburg, AZ 85358
1-800-215-1637

FOREWORD

The purpose of this book is not to remove the mystique or to tarnish the glitter of gold, but rather to shed light for the layman on the histories and mysteries of gold. The view is from the eye of the beholder. The author, Robert Barefoot, is a research analytical chemist who, when he extracted gold in the mid 1970s and found that it was in the form of 18 micron (much less than 1,000th of an inch) octahedral crystals, realized that all of the conventional gravity systems of extraction would be useless. Realizing that another force must be applied, he developed a high-force mini swirl system that forced the positively charged gold particles so close to their negatively charged collector that the electrical forces could then apply thousands of Gs to the gold particles thereby assuring their entrapment. The concept of differential charging metals in a slurry was *"so new"* (so stated in 1992, according to Al Johnson a 90-year old patent attorney from Stanford, Connecticut who had worked many years with the patent office and was considered to be the most knowledgeable man on patents in America) that in 1990, the U.S. Patent Office had to accept all of the patent claims without a challenge, which never had been done before in the history of the Patent Office. Barefoot's equipment was less than one tenth the size of conventional gold extraction equipment, and one tenth the cost in both dollars and time. Therefore, vigorous pursuit of the patent was warranted. From discovery to development, the research required to prepare the first patent application, a British Provisional Patent, took ten years with field tests all over North America.

Because gold mining is filled with flaws and failures, everything that could go wrong did go wrong, and then some. The gold technology research and development operations were flooded out, burned out, and closed down by wild Kodiak grizzly bears; shut down due to incorrect ore assessment; shut down by environmental bureaucrats; shut down by theft; shut down by extortion; shut down by a well orchestrated gold scam; and last but not least, shut down by success. The latter ocurred on a Yukon placer where, on many days, the gold lost in the tailings was 10 times greater than the gold recovered in the sluice box, and the recoveries from running only one tenth of the tailings through the new system were greater than the total gold recovered in the sluice box. Because the equipment was not ready for patenting (there were high wear factors on the equipment) and because of the fact that any attempt at commercial production would be deemed as *"public disclosure,"* which would negate the patent application, the opportunity was reluctantly refused and the operation shut down.

In the process of attempting to commercialize the technology, interaction occurred with some of the most colorful people in the gold industry, including the presidents of some of America's largest mines, three billionaires, and numerous gold scam artists, one of whom was world class. In addition, tests were run in the jungles of Costa Rica and Ghana. There was never a dull moment: shootings, snakes, fist fights, and one moment where the author—who doesn't drink hard liquor—was forced at spear point in the jungle in Ghana to "chug-a-lug" a quart of schnapps without breathing. The latter was part of a ceremonial by the chief to consummate his extortion.

Unfortunately, the acceptance of new technology by the gold industry sometimes takes decades. Currently, negotiations are underway with the largest mining corporations in the world to test the technology in both Venezuela, Panama and South Africa. Success with these projects should launch the technology into the 21st century when most of the worlds gold will be produced using it.

PREFACE

For several years, Mr. Barefoot worked in the petroleum industry and the mining industry. Then one day, by accident he discovered that most gold in ores takes the form of an 18 micron (less than one thousandth of an inch) octahedral crystal, which is the form of preference for high-pressure and high-temperature crystallization (from the bowels of the earth). His claim was initially disputed by the so-called "gold experts," who later recanted their objection when Barefoot developed techniques (electroamalgamation) to recover the golden micron crystals and then melt them into indisputable gold bars. The recognition of the shape and size of the crystals led Barefoot to conclude that all conventional gravity systems for the recovery of gold did not even have a remote chance of working. When he reinforced this conclusion by using famous hydro-geologist Hjulstom's Diagram of Velocity of Water Versus Deposition, he demonstrated that thousands of Gs (one G is the force of gravity) would be required. He then set out on a program to use high force mini swirls to force the positively charged micron gold so close to a negatively charged collector that the electrical force of attraction provided thousands of Gs of force.

Although the initial tests were all very successful, the development of the technology into a patentable entity took over 10 years of frustrating research, with field-testing all over North America . Equally frustrating has been the ten years that have elapsed since the first patent application where the gold industry's extraordinary high rate of failure combined with numerous people in the industry with a vested interest in maintaining the status quo, preventing exploitation of the technology. Historically, this reluctance to accept new technology will eventually be overcome as the technology gradually becomes accepted. The efforts to succeed have continued to the point where the chief executives of the world's largest mining companies are now reviewing the technology. The day will therefore soon come when the differential recovery system will be the main process, not only in the recovery of gold, but also diamonds and other metals. It will also be employed in the environmental clean-up of toxic metals.

So sit back and relax in a comfortable chair, and prepare to enjoy the informative and exciting story of gold: the metal that glitters in the hearts of mankind.

ACKNOWLEDGEMENT

The author is grateful and wishes to acknowledge his appreciation for the dedication, contributions, and efforts of Frank and Elaine Downey, Bruce and Carole Downey, Bill and Jackie Edgecombe, and the author's wife Karen and family who not only assisted in the completion, editing and critical review of this book, but all of whom were active participants in the Story of Gold. Also, the author wishes to acknowledge the critical review of the book by Brett Davies and Elana and Norm Zimmerman. Thanks, guys.

If It Glitters *by Bob Barefoot*

The stakes are high, and some men die,
While others milk their brothers,
They would sell their souls, and flash bank rolls,
Then stop to sell their mothers.

They're blinded by light, that shines day and night,
The blazing yellow that glitters,
And though they're told that "it's only gold,"
They become wild and vicious critters.

Wars have been fought, men of stature been bought,
Just to possess this precious metal,
And men become apes, with tortures and rapes,
Un-human like the flower without petal.

And when gold is found, these men are bound,
By the greed for metal and glitter,
They'll spend it fast, it will not last,
And foul the Earth with their litter.

But there are a few, with hearts so true,
That know of this pending disaster,
The dangerous glitter, that drive men bitter,
To bring on old age, so much faster.

And these men who care, are really so rare,
They just want the gold for their brothers,
And when they find the gold, the story is told,
They quickly go home to their mothers.

But it cost more than it's worth, to dig in the earth,
And tunnel from level to level,
Searching for gold, men quickly turn old,
Most selling their souls to the devil.

TABLE OF CONTENTS

NOTATION

It is not the intent of this book to demean or criticize the majority of professionals in the gold or copper industries, as they have been working hard with the best technology available to them. The problem lies with the few closed minded and blind experts who, by perpetuating the status quo for their own security or financial gain, are holding up the mainstream in accepting the new technology of the 21st century. By introducing the concept of new technology to the mainstream, it is hoped that they both embrace and further develop it, as it satisfies the concerns of both financial and time economics in the gold industry, and also the justifiable concerns of the environmental community.

CHAPTER ONE

HOW MUCH GOLD IS THERE ON EARTH ?

To begin with, gold is one of the 98 naturally occurring elements that make up the universe as we know it. Gold is an element that stands out above all others because in its pure elemental metallic form, it is one of the heaviest substances known to man, and it shines bright yellow and glitters in the sunlight, never tarnishing. It has been revered and worshipped since the beginning of recorded history, and probably since the beginning of time known to man.

Today, gold experts believe that the earth's crust holds more than 4,000,000,000,000,000 (or 4,000 trillion) ounces of gold (which is a 10-mile depth of lithosphere at 5 parts per billion), but the actual amount is probably many times that amount as the Earth's crust is many times thicker than 10 miles and it has never been analyzed by man. The world's gold vaults currently hold about 4,000,000,000 ounces, or about one millionth of the total gold that the experts claim is contained in the Earth's crust. It is estimated that twice this amount is held by individuals around the world. This may seem like a large amount, but because of the density, all of the gold in the vaults could be put into a 60-foot by 60-foot by 60-foot container. All of the gold in the earth's crust would fill a container with the dimensions of 6,000 feet by 6,000 feet by 6,000 feet. We have hardly even begun to tap this huge resource. However, it should be remembered that the definition of an *"expert"* is one who knows so much about a specific area of interest, that his opinion on the subject is almost invariably right. This is sort of like the horse wearing visors: the horse can see everything a long distance in front, however , the horse is blind to everything happening on his flanks. This is also similar to the *"ivory tower syndrome"* where the professor, who remains cocooned in his academic towers, is never subjected to the opinions of the common man, and therefore remains ignorant to events in the real world. When it comes to credibility, gold experts may have to take back seats to the weathermen who can only accurately predict the weather a few hours ahead of time. The joke in the gold industry is that for every 100 gold mining prospects recommended by the experts, the experts should have said no to all 100, and in doing so, would have only been wrong only once, as less than 1% of recommended gold ventures are financially successful. The expert is therefore the only one guaranteed to make money. And, as for the amount of gold contained in the world's crust, the expert's opinion is still more than likely less than 1% correct, meaning that the actual amount could be as much as 100 fold greater.

Experts believe that the average content of gold in the 286 million cubic miles of the world's oceans is 0.012 parts per billion. About 0.003 parts per billion is found in fresh water, between 2 and 56 parts per billion in hot springs, and between 0.1 and 31 parts per billion in salty lakes. This calculates out to about 460 billion ounces, which would fill a container of 300 feet by 300 feet by 300 feet, and is over 100 times the gold currently held in the world's vaults.

Thus, being so apparently plentiful in the lithosphere and oceans of the world, one would expect gold to be found almost everywhere in small amounts, ***and it is!*** When gold is present in the soil, plant roots absorb the gold which then accumulates in the plant's proteins and chlorophyll, a chemical compound which makes the plant green. The roots of plants can even break up rock, liberating the gold for uptake by the plants. This is especially true in arid regions where the roots must break up rocks to liberate the contained structured water (structured water is not a liquid, but rather a solid part of the crystal matrix; gypsum, which is calcium sulfate dehydrate, contains up to 27% water in its dry powder form). When the animals eat the plants, the gold accumulates in the protein rich substances, such as hair, liver, brains and muscles. Man not only eats the plants and bread made from the ***"golden wheat,"*** but also then eats the animals who ate the gold. Gold can be found in man's liver, brain and muscle. Gold in human blood has been measured up to 0.8 parts per billion, and amounts up to 43 parts per billion have been found in human hair. Human feces and urine have been known to contain startling amounts of gold; the ash of human excretion has been known to contain up to one-third of an ounce (10,000 parts per billion) per ton. Although this is equivalent to a high-grade ore, it takes over 30 tons of feces to produce 1 ton of feci ash. At $300.00 per ounce of gold, the human feci contains about $3.00 per ton, which makes extraction uneconomical, if not unsavory.

Other unusual sources of gold have been found in Russian wine at 0.76 parts per billion, marine organisms at 245 parts per billion, Czechoslovakian june bugs at 25,000 parts per billion (ashed), bees at 400 parts per billion (ashed), birds up to 1,500 parts per billion (ashed), deer antlers up to 69,000 parts per billion, up to 3 parts per billion in asphalt, 1000 parts per billion in tar sands, 0.01 parts per billion in rain water, and even air has 3 millionths of one part per billion. Thus, gold can be found everywhere in small quantities; however, almost everyone—except the experts—has trouble finding it. Perhaps that is why God made gold so distinctively brilliantly yellow. However, finding gold that is *"economically extractable,"* which means that it must be produced at substantially less than the current price of $300.00 per ounce, is quite another matter. *The experts usually fail.* In fact, gold experts are so pessimistic that if they reject 100 out of 100 gold projects, they know that they will only have been *wrong once.* And yet, despite these odds, millions are lured into the gold fields.

CHAPTER TWO

IN THE BEGINNING

Gold was definitely among the first metals known to man. The Bible tells us that next to the Garden of Eden is *"Havilah, where, there is gold."* The first man to find this unique substance must have been attracted by its glitter in the water of a creek, possibly in a mountainous region. As soon as he picked up the shining object, most probably a gold nugget, to examine it, he knew immediately that he had found something special. Never before had he found anything so small that weighed so much. He could not wait to show his find to his friends, who curiously passed it from hand to hand. Then, in primitive fashion, one of them bit down hard on the nugget. To everyone's amazement, a shiny groove appeared where the tooth had made its indentation. Soon everyone took a turn biting this extraordinary piece of metal, laughing while they determined who could make the biggest and brightest dent. All of a sudden, one of the men got an idea and placed the grooved piece of metal on a large flat rock and then smashed it with another rock. To everyone's amazement, the small piece of metal became flat and shinier than ever. As everyone took turns smashing the metal with heavy stones, the metal grew larger, flatter, and even shinier. A game then pursued to determine just how much smashing the metal could endure before it would break. But, the metal just grew thinner, flatter and larger with every smash, as these ancients had no idea that just one ounce of gold could be beaten down to a 300 square foot sheet. Soon their metal became fist size, outgrowing the rocks used to smash it, until finally they realized that the metal was not going to break. With every smash of the rock on the metal, each man resolved to himself that he would like to possess this piece of metal. Thus began one of the most basic instincts for mankind, the quest for gold. A search of the area where the nugget had been found proved fruitless. There was no more glitter to be found. This made the man who had found the now flattened piece of gold even more possessive of his find, turning down numerous offers to trade. Finally, he succumbed to a more than generous offer, and mankind entered a new era, bartering with gold.

It was a long time before another piece of gold was found, and when it was, a fight for it ensued. It was reasoned that if man wanted to possess gold so badly, then the gods must also want to possess gold. This meant that in order to barter with the gods in the next life, it would be advisable to have gold with you. Thus began the practice of being buried with the gold you possess. The royal leaders of these primitive groups had decreed that only they could possess gold, as it would ensure their divinity. From the very beginning, gold was considered to be the rightful property of kings and queens and the very wealthy. The eternal quest for gold had begun.

The first gold produced in any quantity was undoubtedly placer or alluvial gold. This is gold that had been liberated from rocks by the action of glaciers or water, and transported by water to be deposited in the cracks, dips and crevices of creeks and rivers. Man soon learned which environment of deposition to look in to find golden nuggets. It did not take long to discover that the further upstream they went, the larger and more abundant the nuggets. Gold was quickly recognized to have originated high up in the mountains. As man mined the upper reaches of the gold nugget streams, the gold abruptly disappeared. Searching the nearby rocks soon unveiled that the shiny metal could be seen stuck inside the white rock outcrops. Smashing away at these outcrops with large rocks proved to be a lot of work and yielded very little gold. Thus, for the thousands of years to follow, placer gold from streams remained the main source of gold.

Golden artifacts that were made over 40,000 years ago by sun worshippers were found in Spain. Then, about 4,000 BC (6,000 years ago), man found that metal could be melted and poured into molds, producing any number of desired shapes. The first golden crown was probably poured around this time. Tools made from iron were invented and quickly became popular. This also made it much easier to remove gold from its source rocks, especially by using the then readily available slaves. Hard-rock gold mining began in earnest. Gold quickly became more prevalent, especially with royalty, who deemed that the metal could only be possessed by the gods, or by royalty or by royal consent.

Somewhere around 7,000 BC (about 9,000 years ago), the emperor of China heard that a farmer possessed geese that *laid golden eggs*. Indeed, the farmer had found substantial amounts of gold while cleaning out his goose pens. The Emperor visited the farmer and watched as he cleaned his pens and recovered gold. The Emperor utilized his royal rights and took the geese back to his palace where they abruptly stopped *laying golden eggs*. The farmer was summoned to the palace where he failed to induce the geese to lay more gold. His head was summarily chopped off and the geese were eaten. Meanwhile back at the farm, the local farmers remained silent as they cleaned their goose pens and recovered the gold nuggets which their geese had eaten from the mountain stream beds and then excreted in their pens. Since this time, there have been numerous reports of gold nuggets being found in both bird crops and bird droppings all over the world. Meanwhile, over the 9,000 years that followed, children all over the world listen intently as they are told the fable of the goose that *laid the golden egg.*

The pyramidal towers of Sumeria, in about 3,000 BC (5,000 years ago) were each topped by as much as 50 tons of gold. King Solomon of Israel, (970 to 930 BC, 3,000 years ago) obtained most of his gold—which he used lavishly for such things as furniture—from Ophir, which is now commonly known as King Solomon's Mines. A few hundred years later, Greek mythology records that King Midas was granted one wish by the gods. Since, for centuries, man had been trying to perfect alchemy, which was the creation of gold from other metals, King Midas made the wish that everything he touched turn gold. His wish was granted, hence the expression *the Midas Touch*. When his food and drink turned into gold, King Midas had to then beg the gods to revoke his wish This myth fueled the fires for alchemy which has continued to the present.

The Persian Empire, followed by the Greek Empire, followed by the Roman Empire all sponsored expeditions all over the world seeking locations for slaves to mine gold, or to plunder the gold already mined, which was usually found in the graves of other emerging cultures. The potentates of the Persians, Greeks and Romans would lavish gold upon themselves, with the current empire plundering the previous empire. Yet no empire was more famous than the Egyptian Empire, the civilization that remained at home to mine its gold. The expression *Cleopatra and her golden fleece* is still well known today, but incorrectly conjures Cleopatra lavishing gold upon herself in the form of gold-woven clothing. In reality, Egyptian Queen Cleopatra led a civilization that discovered that by lining their sluice boxes with sheep skin, a large amount of fine gold could be recovered. The sheepskins were hung up in trees to dry before shaking out the gold. Realizing that the Nile River contained many of Mother Nature's largest sluice boxes, Cleopatra had certain spots in the river (when the river was at its lowest yearly level) lined with thousands of sheep skins sewn together. After one year, she had the sheepskins removed and replaced with new ones. The removed sheep skins were so laden with gold that it could not be shaken out. Instead, she had the sheepskins burned, and the gold was panned from the ashes. The recovery of what had been previously unrecoverable—fine powder gold in placers— made Cleopatra one of the most successful gold miners in history.

Probably, from the earliest dynasty, it was discovered that *electrum*, a naturally occurring gold-silver alloy, would cause drinks laced with arsenic-the favored poison to kill kings—to fizz and produce bubbles and a scum at the surface of the drink. Needless to say, almost all drinks consumed by royalty—even to this day—are from cups made from electrum. Current royalty makes the claim that they are just trying to maintain a royal tradition. This is probably true, as drinking from electrum cups is *the tradition of staying alive*.

As usually is the case when history is discussed, it is usually discussed from the perspective of the white culture only, and when it comes to the history of gold, this is an obvious travesty. The Chinese have always been sought for their gold mining expertise because of their success at mining gold for thousands of years. The Chinese, along with Native Americans—who also have thousands of years of successful gold mining history—have always become the culture of choice to make into slaves for gold mines. In most cases they willingly became slaves, as they also had the expertise to be the best gold thieves in the world. The next culture of choice for gold slavery would be miners from India, whose culture to this day revere and prize all objects made from gold. In all these cultures, it is considered sacrilegious to remove gold from the dead. Thus as in other cultures where royalty always possesses massive amounts of gold, the gold in the graves is safest with the local cultures. This is despite the temptation provided by the massive amounts of gold buried. For example, in the 14th Century BC, King Tutankhamen was buried in a solid gold coffin that was filled with 36,000 ounces of gold. This would make him a *dead billionaire* thus dispelling the old myth that *"you can't take it with you."* Also, for thousands of years, incredibly large amounts of gold, found by the Indians of North, Central and South America, was buried in their graves when they died, most of which was possessed by the chiefs and the Indian kings.

CHAPTER THREE

GOLD AND CHRISTOPHER COLUMBUS

Unfortunately, the best white gold miners—the Spanish conquerors—mined most of their gold by plundering graves. For over 10,000 years, the Indians of North, Central and South America had been collecting gold to take to their graves, making easy targets for our white hero explorers to plunder. They were led by Christopher Columbus, who in 1492, had reached and explored what today is known as the Bahamas, the Greater Antilles, and Cuba. Initially, Columbus refused to believe that what is now known as the West Indies was not Asia. After trading trinkets for gold, Columbus left 39 men to continue his endless search for more gold while he returned to Spain. The Indians soon tired of trinkets. The golden treasures buried in the Indian graves must have proved too big a temptation, for when Columbus returned in 1493 to ravish the Indian gold with his 17 ships and 2,000 men, he found his fort burned to ashes and all of the men he had left were dead. Columbus quickly built a new fort 70 miles away near a mountain pass leading to what his log book describes as *an interior glistening with gold*. In 1494,some of Columbus's men cut the ear off of an Indian chief who refused to trade his gold. They then began cutting one ear off every child over the age of fourteen declaring that "if the child wanted to keep his remaining ear, he would pay Columbus 3 ounces of gold every month" Of course, the peace-loving Indians retaliated against these barbaric acts.

Columbus continued to seek the source of what his log book described as *King Solomon's golden riches*, and in 1502, on the coast of Central America, he thought that he had found it, reporting in his log book that *"Either it is Ophir (King Solomon's Mines) or Cipangu."* Columbus named his discovery *"Costa Rica"*, which means *"rich coast"* because of the thousands of Indians adorned with heavy gold ornaments which dangled from their necks and arms. While trading trinkets for the gold, Columbus learned of more gold and an ocean on the other side of the mountains. With a staggering bounty of gold in his ships' hold, Columbus extracted an oath from each of his men *"never to mention the wealth of Costa Rica,"* thereby ensuring exactly the opposite to occur, the wildfire spread of the information throughout Europe.

On February 24, 1503, Columbus began building the first settlement in mainland North America on the mouth of the river Bele in Costa Rica. Columbus soon learned that the Indians tiring of trading for trinkets and fearing for their ancestral graves, just as the Indians—in the Indies had done—were talking about setting fire to the houses and killing the white Christians who would do anything to rob them of their cherished treasures of gold Columbus decided to *punish the Indians*. As an example and deterrent to neighboring Indians, Columbus ordered his brother to capture the king of all of the Indians, as well as several of the tribal chiefs. Over 50 of the unsuspecting Indian leaders were captured and put in the hold of a ship anchored in the harbor, while Columbus was presented with a booty of golden artifacts stolen from the King's house. The ingenious Indians piled the rocks that were used for the ship's ballast and that were found in the ship's hold into a cone-like structure that reached the hatch on the ship's deck. The king, along with most of the chiefs, escaped, while those who were re-captured were quickly hanged on the deck of the ship while the Indians on shore watched. The Indians, who vastly outnumbered Columbus and his men, retaliated by attacking the settlers who had to quickly retreat to the safety of the ships.

Columbus returned to Spain, his ships weighted down with the gold stolen from Indian graves. The king of Spain wanted more gold, and so he sent more ships and more soldiers back to America with Columbus. Indians were massacred and those who survived were subjected to the Columbus practice of having one ear chopped off. They watched as Columbus men looted the graves of their ancestors, while Columbus continued his search for the elusive *Eldorado*, the illusive source of all of the gold.

Columbus, who had started a war with the Indians that would last for centuries and who had introduced these peace-loving and mild-mannered people to torture, failed in his efforts to colonize the mainland. He soon found himself confronted by greedy rivals who were eager to plunder the gold from Indian graves, and who therefore sought to discredit Columbus. It worked, as Columbus's efforts to find Eldorado did not produce much gold, and he had also failed in his quest to colonize the mainland. Columbus quickly fell into disfavor with the king and was *returned to Spain in chains*. In 1506, to the joy of every American Indian, Columbus died in humiliation. Fortunately for Columbus, he is only remembered for his discovery of the New World, and not for the *lust for gold* that fueled his exploits and his incredible brutality accompanied by centuries of death and suffering of the American Indian. The 16th century saw 24,000,000 ounces of gold removed from Indian graves. *Shame! Shame! Shame!*

Christopher Columbus by Bob Barefoot

In 1492, Christopher Columbus sailed the ocean blue,
And to the quest for gold, he promised to be true,
So when the Indians were found with lots of gold,
He traded for trinkets with both young and old.

Then chopped off one ear from each Indian Child,
Who watched as gold fever make white men go wild,
Three ounces per month is what they were told,
Or the other ear comes off, as we need more gold.

He plundered the gold from their ancestral graves,
While seeking Eldorado in the hills and the caves,
He then turned the ocean into a sea of red,
With Indian blood as he slaughtered them dead.

The greed for gold helped his rivals to flourish,
But the King's appetite for gold he failed to nourish,
Thus humiliated and shunned, he soon died in Spain,
Columbus, the man who had taught the Indians pain.

CHAPTER FOUR

GOLD IN THE AMERICAS

The American Indians have been mining gold for thousands of years. They have been routinely forced into slavery to mine for gold in North, Central, and South America, especially by the Spanish. Since the time of Columbus, Indians have learned from the white man and adopted his practice of chopping off body parts for which they were called *savages*. In the beginning they believed that the white men who routinely used this practice must also fear it. Thus, for the brutality imposed on the Indian by the white man, such as chopping the ears off of live Indians, the Indians began to retaliate by chopping the scalps off of dead Spaniards.

The Spanish were impeded from mining the northern parts of North America by the English and French settlers who, although they had the same weakness for gold, were more interested in exploiting the lucrative fur trade in Europe. The fur trade prospered in the far north, which was lush with trees and animals. The farther north the settlers trapped, the more fur they attained, and the fewer problems they had with the native Indians with whom the settlers traded for fur. Here, the Indians gladly worked with the settlers in the bountiful fur trade. This was in contrast to their brothers to the south who were used as slaves in the gold trade. In the south, the Spanish sought to fill their ship holds with gold and return to Spain to live in luxury. In the North, the English and French had come to settle the land, seeking refuge from political and religious persecution in Europe.

Unfortunately, that did not stop the English and French from adopting the despicable technique developed by the Spaniards of *discovering* Indian gold mines. A popular technique was be to employ the *bait and switch* technique on the unsuspecting Indians. First the *bait;* trade fairly and frequently with the Indians for their gold charms to establish a pattern of trust and reward. Then the *switch;* offer to give the Indians more than they expect, but, for more gold than they could carry at the time, while informing them that the offer will only be open for a short time. The Indians were thereby encouraged to return quickly to their mines to obtain more gold for the trade. Knowing this, the Indians were followed, and when their mines were located, they were then killed, as at this time in history, it was "impossible" to murder Indians as they were not considered people. The result is a white man makes another gold *discovery.* The famous Vulture Gold Mine in Arizona, which produced over a billion dollars worth of gold at today's value, was discovered with this technique by Henry Wickenburg, who subsequently had the nearby town named after him. The only justice that occurred was poetic, as Wickenburg was swindled out of his mine by a man who had enough money to buy the judge. Shortly after, this man, known as Mr. Phelps, created the industrial mining giant Phelps Dodge with his new gold-wealthy son-in-law, Mr. Dodge. Because the lives of Indians had no value, it is unknown just how many gold mines were discovered this way; however, it is safe to bet that up to the late 1800s, the majority of gold mines were discovered, or stolen, by this despicable bait and switch technique. Ironically, because dead and worthless

16

Indians can tell no tales and would never be believed if they did, these ruthless white men became heroes, and like Christopher Columbus and Henry Wickenburg, towns cities and streets have been named after them.

Spaniard Don Juan de Onate was successful in his military conquest of the Indians of New Mexico in 1599. He immediately ordered the amputation of the right foot of 24 of the Acoma Pueblo Indian men. Onate was later stripped of his titles and banished from the colony for his cruelty. Yet today, the Pueblo Indians are forced to live with a large statue honoring Onate the explorer. Nonetheless, the proud, bitter, and subdued Indian of today teaches his children to remember these horrific crimes of the past that were committed against his people by the men the whites honor today. Thus as we celebrate Columbus Day, the Indians quietly remember him for his barbaric acts against their people.

In the late 1700s the first gold mined in America by the English white community was in what is now known as North Carolina. The lure of gold caused all of the early North American explorers to be on the lookout for the precious metal. Whenever gold was found, or discovered , a *gold rush* of thousands of overnight gold miners would flood the region, causing tension and retaliation by the history-hardened Indians. The flood of white men chased out the game the Indians needed to survive. This resulted in the Indians having to steal, and the whites, retaliating by slaughtering the Indians. The lure of easy-to-find gold created instant gold rush towns that sprang up all over the American west, and the towns that serviced them, such as San Francisco, also flourished. The largest was the California gold rush of 1849 spawning the gold rush city called Brandy City, which was the largest city west of Chicago at the time. Currently it consists of only three unmarked graves. The gold rush also caused the town of San Francisco to explode into a major city supporting the needs of the gold industry.

In 1849 there were an estimated 150,000 Indians in California. The hoard of gold seekers flooding into Indian lands chased the game away. Desperate Indians were forced to steal livestock from the newcomers, who fought back killing many Indians. In the lawless atmosphere of the time many miners killed the Indians to seize their gold rich lands. Also, the need for skilled gold miners resulted in slave hunters raiding Indian villages, enslaving even the women and children. Most of these enslaved Indians were killed during their mining ordeal. By 1870 the Indian population in California had been reduced to 30,000 (80% had been slaughtered in just 21 years. Shame!). Thus, in 21 years of gold fever, 80% of the Indians in California had been slaughtered.

Another famous gold rush city was Central City Colorado, which sprung up almost overnight in the early 1850s, as both gold and silver was found in abundance for miles around. America's first claims were recorded and registered here. Any shape of claim was allowed: square-shaped claims, rectangles, triangles and star- shaped claims were most common. The famous *Glory Hole*, a mammoth open hole pit with tunnels and trains at the bottom feeding ore to nearby mills, gobbled up most of the early claims. Those who refused to sell out to the constantly expanding mining conglomerate, unfortunately, soon found their claims blasted with dynamite to the bottom of the *Glory Hole*, where the "ore from the sky" was quickly transported to the eagerly awaiting mills. Nothing was too lavish for the newly rich Americans of Central City. They even replaced the cobble stones leading to their opera house with gold and silver bars prior to the visit by the President of the United States.

The 1850s saw several gold rush towns spring up in California, most after gold nuggets were found in nearby mountain streams. Most of these towns became the abandoned *ghost towns* you can find on today's maps. Some are nonexistent today. For example, a few graves hidden by tall pines is all that now remains of the bustling gold rush town of Brandy City, California, which at its peak was the largest city west of Chicago and was famous for its huge gold nuggets, gunfights, and opera house.

Nearby Downyville, a quaint little tourist town today, is also famous for its large nuggets, most of which were discovered in the famous *tin cup diggings* . It was named so because the Chinese, who were considered to be the best gold miners of the day, were used as slaves to mine the deposit and were each issued one tin cup. They would receive one full cup of rice for each full cup of nuggets that they mined. The white slave masters should have been suspicious, as the Chinese were obviously eager to become mining slaves. However, the quickly filled tin cups, full of nuggets, blurred their vision. The Chinese, with thousands of years experience mining gold, knew that the richness of the deposit would be short lived, and that their greedy slave masters would disappear with the gold. Thus, they worked extra hard and extra long, and although malnourished, managed to hide away an extra tin cup of gold for every tin cup they turned in for rice. When the gold deposit petered out, their masters disappeared on schedule. The so-called ignorant Chinese slaves dug up their booty of gold and headed west where they both bought and built a significant portion of the bustling town known as San Francisco. Gold had made them the richest slaves in history, while robbery, gunfights, and swindling had impoverished most of their former masters.

To the northwest of California lay the Black Hills of South Dakota, which was the sacred hunting grounds of the local Indians, as well as their sacred gold grounds. In 1834, a group of white miners entered the Hills, violating the Indians sacred grounds while also violating the treaty recently signed by the whites. They supposedly *got all the gold that they could carry*, but in reality, they disappeared to the accompaniment of whistling Indian arrows. The same fate met the gold rush miners heading for California, who ventured into the same sacred Hills and who also disappeared. Although geologist Ferdinand Hayden announced to the world that gold could be found in the hills, nothing had more impact than General Custer's subsequent slaughter in the famous ***"Battle of the Little Big Horn"***, which was fought in retaliation for General Custer's recent slaughter of Indian women and children and his violation of the sacred Black Hills Indian grounds. The Indians correctly predicted that the discovery of gold would result in the white man forcefully and illegally taking away their sacred lands. Custer was slaughtered because his violation of Indian sacred grounds in his quest for gold would eventually lead to the loss of their sacred lands. Those who followed in Custer's footsteps used his death to justify their slaughter of the Indians while they plundered the gold from their lands.

 Today, one of the world's largest gold mining companies, Homestake, still prospers, recovering gold from the still sacred Indian lands. The Indians were run off and to this day have received no royalties for the billions of dollars worth of gold recovered from their stolen mines. The town of Deadwood, located in the Black Hills, is more famous for ***the killing of Wild Bill Hickock*** while he was playing a game of cards in a local saloon, than for ***the millions of ounces of gold mined*** by its inhabitants. Today the inhabitants of Deadwood, along with the major property owner, Homestake, are enjoying another gold rush boom. This boom, however, is in the form of legalized gambling which was voted in to raise money to preserve the rich white american history of the Black Hills, the "great General Custer," and the "barbaric Indians." Unfortunately, history is always written by those who win and plunder. Meanwhile, the current residents of Deadwood are finding the slot machines more lucrative than any gold nugget placer of the gold rush days.

 By the 1880s, men had sought out and exploited the easiest and the richest of the shallow gold, which could be found in most of the enriched surface deposits worldwide. These ores were rich enough in free milling gold to be processed in hot, sealed mercury tanks that were lined with copper (usually cooked for about 8 hours with mercury and a few other chemicals added to amalgamate the metallic gold). This procedure was a modification of the *Patio Process*, which will be discussed in detail in the next chapter, and was very popular in North America, right up to the 1890s, when it was replaced by the present day popular cyanide process. One of the more famous amalgam mills was at Eureka in Utah.

To understand how these gold rush early ores became so rich in the *easy to extract* metallic gold, one has to understand the basic geology of gold, or rather, the basic geochemistry of gold. Generally speaking, most gold found within 400 feet of surface with an abundance of water and air is in the metallic or free milling form. Gold and silver found below this level which has little or no water and air, is complexed with sulfides, usually a form of iron sulfide or pyrites. It is suspected that all gold comes from the depths of the earth in the sulfide form. Surface waters containing air, found in the upper 400 feet of depth, cause the sulfides to undergo oxidation changing to sulfates, some of which are soluble. This liberates the gold which is then transported by the surface waters, undergoing natural concentration mechanisms known as surface enrichment, such as placer gold. When ocean waters wash over these ores, the pyrites generate sulfuric acid, which, when mixed with the high salt content (sodium chloride) of the ocean waters, creates some hydrochloric acid. Gold is soluble in this acid and is therefore converted into ionized gold chloride, one of the most soluble forms of gold, which is free to travel until it is neutralized by reacting with the alkaline minerals contained in certain rocks, which—when in the presence of metals, such as zinc or iron—can cause the gold ions to be chemically reduced (gaining electrons) to metallic gold forming an enriched precipitate. However, in other instances, when zinc or iron does not exist in the alkaline rocks, thiosulfates can be produced, resulting in the production of soluble gold thiosulfates. These gold ions are then transported until they can be chemically reduced by the presence of other metal ions, such as iron or zinc. This once again produces a rich precipitate or gold enriched deposit. Thus, massive low grade sulfide gold deposits, exposed to water and air, have more than one mechanism to cause them to become enriched in high grade surface deposits. Most of the gold discovered and mined up to the late nineteenth century was free milling (metallic), surface oxidized gold.

It should be noted that the most common form of gold is the mineral gold chloride, as there is 100 times as much gold in the oceans of the world than all of the surface gold ever mined. The Dead Sea itself, for example, contains more dissolved gold all of the gold ever mined. Organics such as algae, bacteria, fungi fungi and certain other plants can readily absorb the gold in this form. For example, algae has been known to contain up to 1700 parts per billion of gold, and fungi has been measured at 1200 parts per billion. Activated charcoal can absorb many times its weight in ionized gold, and hence is used in many commercial extraction plants. The roots of hardy desert plants can disintegrate the surrounding rock, thereby liberating both structured water and chemically entrapped gold. These plants, which absorb much of this liberated gold, are often used in geochemical surveys in the search for gold. Another common occurrence of gold absorption, although much less understood, is the absorption of gold by clays or their sister gels. Both have a very negatively charged edge surface that strongly attracts positive gold ions.

Unfortunately, by the 1880s, most of the surface-enriched ores all over the world had been mined out, and the less rich, yet massive sulfide gold ores beneath did not respond to the extraction by mercury or the Patio Process. At this time, a jeweler had accidentally placed his gold watch in a dish which contained some dissolved cyanide, The result was the rapid removal of the gold plating on the watch. Gold extraction by cyanidation was born. Engineers quickly discovered that the sulfide gold also dissolved in the cyanide solution, allowing for the first time in history, the easy and inexpensive extraction of gold from massive low-grade deposits, which quickly became the primary targets of the gold industry. The gold dissolved in the cyanide solutions was precipitated as *gold mud* by the addition of inexpensive zinc metal. Thus, a new era in gold mining began. The spotty surface enriched gold deposits and the hot mercury gold mills were both abandoned in favor of the massive and consistent sulfide ores, and cyanide plants became an overnight sensation. Only modest improvements in the process were made over the following 100 years. No new process has ever been successfully used to extract gold from ores.

Initially, the gold industry had to be content with processing the low-grade ores. Then, at the turn of the twentieth century, a new concentration procedure was discovered which revolutionized the gold mining industry. It was called *froth flotation*. Oils, to which the gold sulfides adhered, were injected into an aqueous mixture of the pulverized ore, and then air was bubbled up through the mixture, creating bubbles to which the sulfide-laden oil would stick. The gold-rich froth created at the surface was then scooped off, resulting in the production of a rich gold concentrate which dramatically reduced the amount of material which had to be cyanided. Froth flotation was *"discovered"* according to the patent office, back in the 1860s, by a a Montana housewife who noticed the glitter in the bubbles created when washing her husband's mining garb. She scooped it off and showed it to her husband who immediately recognized that his wife had concentrated the previously un-concentratable ore. After a year or so of perfecting the process, a patent was applied for and granted.

Unfortunately, the mining industry was only involved in the unresponsive, enriched free gold deposits at this time. The patent lapsed before the mining industry, desperate for a solution to the high costs of cyaniding the total ore, "discovered" the process in the patent office in the early 1900s. Within three years the whole world was using the process while marveling at the "ingenuity" that led "their engineers" to develop such a process (which in reality was developed and patented by a housewife), which to this day has changed little. These engineers get ***undue credit*** for the development of the cyanide process (which in reality was developed and patented by a jeweler.) Except for cosmetics, ***gold technology has not improved for the last 100 years.***

CHAPTER FIVE

THE PATIO PROCESS

In the early 16th Century, the Spanish were taught that, when exploring for gold, they should always look for mercury which could be readily visible identified and that was always associated with gold. With the ships arriving full of bullion from Columbus's new found Indies, tremendous interest in gold was sparked amongst the whole Spanish population. Numerous groups became keenly interested in improving the efficiency of gold extraction from ores. At the time, ore that had been broken and crushed by dropping it long distances and smashing it with other ore, was then pulverized to a powder in an ***errastre*** to liberate the gold. An errastre consisted of a circular stone patio surrounded by a 3-to 4-foot stone wall. The ore inside on the patio was pulverized by a large, heavy stone wheel. A long pole went through its center and was attached to a swivel pole in the center of the patio. The other end extended over the wall and was attached to a team of donkeys. As the donkeys walked continually around the parameter of the patio, the stone was manually pushed back and forth along the pole to allow the stone to crush all of the ore. The ore was then taken to large vats where it was rolled with water and mercury to amalgamate the gold. The heavy gold and mercury amalgams were then separated by sluicing or washing in a long wooden box with riffles to trap the amalgams.

By this time in history; many were experienced enough that they could make a good guess as to the gold content just by looking at the ore. This was always confirmed by assaying the ore with assay procedures that had been handed down over the centuries. Thus, by the early 1530s, the gold recoveries had been maximized by assaying to assure that only the highest grade of ore was kept in the errastre. Occasionally, the errastre was over-filled, and ore spilled over the wall. The Spaniards soon found that the gold outside of the wall usually assayed much higher than the same ore inside of the errastre. They suspected that the donkeys tramping on the ore on the outside must have something to do with the phenomenon, so they put the donkeys inside of the wall and added more water to disperse the buildup of donkey excretion. Once the ore was pulverized to a smooth paste, determined by an expert rubbing the ore paste against an ear lobe, mercury was added, resulting in an effective amalgamation that eliminated the difficult vat amalgamation procedure. The placement of the donkeys inside of the errastre caused the recovery of gold to increase dramatically, reflecting the higher assays attained by the donkey tramping outside the errastre. At some point in time, fresh water was unavailable, so sea water was used. To their amazement, substantial amounts of silver began being amalgamated along with the gold. Noticing that more silver was extracted whenever copper was present in the ore, Spanish everywhere, especially in where is now Mexico, began to add copper salts, such as the beautifully blue copper sulfate, until they finally perfected the timing and salt addition that yielded the most gold and silver. Thus, the procedure that was to produce the majority of the world's gold and silver over the next 350 years, *the patio process*, was born.

The Spaniards were the first white men to explore the rivers and streams of the newly discovered Americas, and thereby were rewarded with the readily exposed nuggets. They were also the first to tread over the sacred Indian burial grounds that held the vast treasure troves of gold that initially filled their ship's holds before returning to Europe. As this source petered out, it was quickly replaced by Indian slave gold mines. When the ore was not the readily sluiceable free milling gold, the Spanish set up and taught the patio process to their Indian slaves.

The patio process became more famous and more commonly used as time passed. By the 1800s, almost all of the gold and silver produced from Mexico to South America was done so using the patio process. For ores that contained silver only, the patio process was used exclusively.

The patio process, although obviously very successful in extracting gold and silver, had one drawback. From the start of the process to the finish, a total of six weeks was required. This to many was too long, Thus, it was in 1813 that a brilliant and later to be famous chemist named Gay Lusac was commissioned to lead a team of the world's best scientists to try to cut the time required by the patio process in half, thereby allowing the production of the world's most valued commodities—gold and silver—to potentially double. Although modest improvements were developed over the many years of experimentation that followed, absolutely no improvement was made in shortening the time required to process. Gay Lusac worked out most of the basic chemistry that occurred during the process however, there was a major gap in his understanding of the overall process. For example, Lussac knew that mercury reduced the silver chloride, found naturally in the mineral cerarayrite into the element silver (see equation #1):

#1 $AgCl$ + Hg ---------------> Ag + $HgCl$
    silver + mercury   silver + mercurous
    chloride   metal   chloride

Lussac also knew that copper metal caused the mercurous chloride to covert back to mercury metal which could then amalgamate the silver metal (see equation #2):

#2 Cu + $2HgCl$ -------------> $2Hg$ + $CuCl_2$
    copper + mercurous   mercury   copper
    metal   chloride   metal   chloride

However, back in 1604 in what is now present day Bolivia, a Spanish priest and metallurgist, Albero Alfonso Bab, did manage to speed up the chemical reaction on a very rich silver ore by mixing the mercury ore slurry in a large vat lined with copper and then heating the mixture with a fire beneath the pot. Lussac knew that the procedure took only 24 hours; however, the procedure was only effective on specific and rare ores that were extremely rich in silver. Thus he knew that copper metal and heat could help speed up the process of extracting silver from the normal low-grade ores, but this did not explain why the silver recovery of the average ore was always higher than the assay of the cerargyrite (silver mineral) content made possible, and in addition, there was no explanation for the very efficient amalgamation of gold, much of which was not in the readily amalgamatable metallic form in the ores. What Lussac did not know was that mixing the ore with air and water caused the iron sulfides (mostly in the form of pyrite minerals) to break down forming sulfuric acid and hydrated iron oxides (see equation #3):

#3 FeS_2 + $4H_2O$ + $3.5O_2$ -----> $2H_2SO_4$ + $Fe(OH)_2.H_2O$
    pyrite   water   oxygen   sulfuric   hydrated iron
                                acid   oxide

and that the addition of salt water to the resultant ore mixture resulted in the production of hydrochloric acid (see equation #4):

#4 $2NaCl$ + H_2SO_4 --------> $2HCl$ + $NaSO_4$
sodium   sulfuric   hydrochloric   sodium
chloride   acid   acid   sulfate

Silver metal and numerous silver minerals readily dissolve in sulfuric acid to form a soluble silver sulfate (see equation #5):

#5 Ag + H_2SO_4 ------> $2Ag_+$ + $(SO_4)_{--}$ + $2(H)_+$
silver   sulfuric   silver   sulfate   hydrogen
metal   acid   ions   ions   ions

Gold and many gold minerals readily dissolve in hydrochloric acid, especially in the presence of iron oxides (see equation #6):

#6 Au + HCl + $Fe(OH)_x$ ----> $(Au)_+$ + $(Cl)_-$ + H_2O
gold   hydrochloric   iron   gold   chloride   water
metal   acid   oxides   ions   ions

Although Gay Lusac was unaware of these latter two reactions, even knowledge of their occurrence would not be enough to explain why their rate of reaction could not be improved.

T he answer to the mystery lies in the existence of a substance that was discovered one hundred years later. Although Lusac was aware that the donkey urine had introduced uric acid to the slurry, he was unaware of the introduction of *bacteria* and the consequences it would have. He was also equally unaware that the donkey excretion would quickly produce *ammonia*. Today it is well understood that certain species of bacteria feed on sulfur compounds and that the bacterial breakdown of the sulfides in the patio process, which helped to liberate both gold and silver, required a specific amount of time that could not be altered. (see equations #7, 8, 9):

#7 $AuFeS_2$ + bacteria + NH_3 -------> Au
gold   ammonia   gold
sulfides   gas   metal

#8 Au_2S + bacteria + H_2O --------> Au
      gold   water   gold
      sulfides   metal

#9   AgS + bacteria + NH_3 -------> Ag
      silver   ammonia   silver
      argentite   gas   metal

The ammonia from the donkey excretion oxidizes to form nitrates (see equation #10):

#10 $(NH)_4{}^+$ + $3O_2$ + H_2O --------> $(NO_4)^-$ + $3H_2O$
      ammonium oxygen water   nitrate   water
      ion   gas   ion

Next, the nitrates mixed with the sulfuric acid produced from equation #3 resulting in the production of nitric acid (see equation #11):

#11 $2(NO_4)^-$ + H_2SO_4 ------> $2HNO_3$ + $(SO_4)^{--}$ + O_2
      nitrate   sulfuric   nitric   sulfate   oxygen
      ion   acid   acid   ion   gas

Not only is the metal, silver, extremely soluble in nitric acid (see equation # 12):

#12 Ag + HNO_3 + O_2 ---------> $(Ag)^+$ + $(NO_4)^-$
      silver   nitric   oxygen   silver   nitrate
      metal   acid   ion   ion

but also, when nitric acid from equation #11 combines with the hydrochloric acid from equation #4, the result is the production of extremely corrosive aqua regia acid which can readily dissolve most minerals thereby liberating the contained metals as ions, such as silver and gold ions (see equation # 13):

#13 $3HCl \cdot HNO_3$ + Au.FeS$_2$ + Ag$_2$S ----> (Au)$_{+++}$ + (Ag)$_+$

      aqua regia   auroferrous argentite   gold   silver

        acid   sulfide   ion   ion

Thus, when the Spaniards put the donkeys inside of their errastre, which they knew would result in a greater production of gold and silver, they unknowingly provided the ore slurry being crushed with powerful chemical ingredients which facilitated the bacteria and ammonia from the donkey excretion ensured the total extraction of the gold and silver metals from the ore The breakdown of the ore over the life span of the bacteria, which could not be sped up. Had Gay Lusac, the best chemist of his day, known about bacteria, he would have realized that, although it is possible to speed up most chemical reactions, it is equally as impossible to speed up the life cycle of a living creature, and he would have saved himself years of unsuccessful experimentation.

CHAPTER SIX

CLAY AND THE
CYANIDE PROCESS

The most common mineral on the surface of the earth—clay—is by definition a hydrated aluminum silicate. It is created when the most common minerals below the surface—granite and feldspars—are exposed to air and water at the surface. Clays are flat plates, like a stack of flat paper, with the outer edges negatively charged. The amount of charge (different for each type of clay) is called its **cation exchange capacity** or CEC. and is measured in milliequivalents per 100 grams of clay. Koalinite, for example, which is used to make pottery, has a CEC of 3, while Montmorillonite, a mucky clay used as a drilling mud in oil wells, has a CEC of 100. Vermiculite, used in water purifiers and greenhouses has a CEC of 300. Clay minerals can be created from minutes to months by the simple addition of water and oxygen to aluminum silicate feldspars, such as granite found next to the quartz gold vein.

By definitition clay is a hydrated aluminum silicate. The addition of water and air to the sodium rich albite feldspar results in the production of 100 CEC montmorillonite. The production of montmorillonite can be dramatically sped up by the addition of alkalis (providing oxygen). Why this scenario is so important is that high CEC clays can readily absorb gold and this commonly occurs during the most widely used gold extraction procedure, which employs alkaline cyanide. Gold adsorbed on the clay is unrecoverable. The geologist, who is trained that it takes millions of years to produce minerals, is unfamiliar with these clay minerals which are produced within minutes. When he sends his quartz gold ore sample, which contained very little feldspar, to the laboratory, he is unaware that there will be a recovery problem in the mill, as the laboratory readily extracts the gold from his feldspar free sample using cyanide. However, in the gold mill, the ore being processed has been diluted with albitic granite wall rock that crumbled into the ore while blasting, or that was unintentionally mined when the vein ribboned, becoming very thin in spots.

The addition of caustic cyanide to ore diluted with albitic feldspars, whether in cyanide tanks or a heap leach pad, quickly produces montmorillonite gels that absorb the positively ionized gold on their negatively charged edges, sometimes as fast as the cyanide can dissolve the gold. The end result is the inefficient extraction of gold,. from these ores. The *"experts"* in the mining industry attribute the disappearance of the gold to a *"thief"* or a *"robber"* in the mixture, which they incorrectly assume takes the form of a zinc precipitate or some organic gold absorber. This ignorance of the correct chemical mechanism has allowed gold thieves to be common in the gold industry for the past 100 years.

The production of the high CEC montmorillonite, which could be reduced or prevented by the addition of common and inexpensive chemicals, not only absorbs the ionized gold, but also, in the case of heap leach, presents an impenetrable barrier to the cyanide solution, thereby preventing contact with the gold ore below. In the case of cyanide tank leaching, the thieves have been inhibited by the addition of chunks of charcoal to the mixture which have a much higher CEC than the Montmorillonite and result in most of the ionized gold absorbing on the charcoal. The chunks of charcoal are readily screened from the ore and the gold thereby recovered. Initially, when the process was developed in the 1920s, the gold processors added pulverized charcoal to their ore slurrries and then floated the charcoal to recover it. However, the chunk charcoal process proved to be a simpler system. This carbon in pulp (CIP) process is effective in recovering about 75 % of the gold, although claims by the gold operator are usually much higher (up to 99 % depending on how the ore and tailings were incorrectly sampled for analysis).

Although CIP is an acceptable solution for a few ores, it does nothing for the massive heap leaching. The real solution would be to inhibit or prevent the production of montmorillonite during the leaching by employing diagenesis, which is the science of mineral alteration. The heap leach pile should be pretreated with mildly acidic solutions containing large amounts of potassium and ammonium with buffers to prevent gelatinous precipitation when the alkaline potassium cyanide solution is later used. Such pretreatments have been used sucessfully in the oil industry to increase the flow of hydrocarbons to the borehole. However, since the "experts" in charge of processing the gold ores are not knowledgeable in this area, they do what experts all over the world do when their oracle authority is threatened, they become thieves themselves, presenting an impenetrable and invisible barrier between the solution and the problem.

CHAPTER SEVEN

GOLD & MONEY

After studying the history of gold over the past 500 years—a history that includes shipload after shipload full to the brim of gold, mostly stolen from Indian graves, being shipped to the kings of Europe—one has to wonder just what did the recipients of this massive wealth do with their ill-gotten fortunes. They had amassed so much wealth, that by the end of the 19th century they should have *owned the world.* Also, at the end of the 19th century, the kings who had amassed their gold mostly from the graves of Indians, were joined by the nouveau-rich: industrialists who were exploiting the new technology of the cyanide extraction of gold to quickly match and surpass the royal reserves of gold. At the turn of the century, these men were generating billions of dollars in gold (hundreds of billions at today's value). The descendants of these men used this wealth to generate more wealth. This means that the true wealth of the world today—industrial, banking, oil or otherwise—originated from this gold.

The gold mining companies in South Africa, the number one gold producing country of the 20th century, have amassed such massive wealth that their extensive and vast holdings all over the world affect the daily life of every human on the planet.

It is therefore not surprising that almost every monetary system in the world is based on the backing of gold reserves, where the paper value of the bank notes is guaranteed by the gold stored in vaults. The United States currently guarantees only a partial backing of its notes with gold, as it does not have enough gold to provide a total backing. Gold is moved from the vault of one country to the vault of another in a game of musical chairs, with those with the biggest trade balance *temporarily* having the biggest cache. Initially, the largest caches of gold belonged to those countries with the largest production of gold from mining. These countries have been gradually replaced by countries that were more successful producing products that resulted from the industrial revolution.

At the end of the 19th century, gold had risen to $18 per troy ounce. This was a lot of money, as a full course steak dinner could be purchased for under one dollar and a home could be purchased for one thousand dollars. The value of gold began to slowly increase and then, at the height of the great depression in 1932, President Roosevelt pegged the price of gold at $32 per troy ounce and declared the price permanently fixed by law. He also declared that it was illegal for individuals to possess gold. This delighted the miners as the price jump spurred a spree of gold mining which lasted until America entered World War II in 1942. At that time, all gold mining operations in the United States were shut down to divert mining production to more strategic metals such as iron and mercury for submarines.

Unfortunately, after the war, inflation had made start-up costs prohibitive and gold mining floundered until the 1960's which saw the deregulation of the price of gold, which instantly doubled to the $60 per ounce range. By the 1970's the price had steadily risen to values over $200 per ounce, due to inflation fueled by the rapidly rising price of oil, which most countries preferred to trade for gold. Then suddenly, the oil crises of the late 1970's combined with the lack of confidence in paper currency brought on by staggering inflation, caused the price of gold to skyrocket to $900 per troy ounce. Thus, the oil producing countries were displacing the gold from the industrial countries. But there was only so much gold that could be shuffled in the world's gold vaults, and the public soon began to put more value on other commodities, resulting in the rapid drop back to the $400 range which reflected the cost of production.

The day, oil-producing countries have been replaced by the high-tech electronic and automotive countries and the public, due to a more secure world resulting from the decline of communism, has put more value on their products than on the security of gold. The result has been the decline of the price of gold to the $300 per ounce range by the late 1990s, which was below the cost of production. This has necessitated the shutdown of large numbers of the less profitable mines around the world. Eventually, the resulting lack of production of gold, combined with the historical world instability cycles, will cause the price to skyrocket once again. Also tempting is the prospect that gold valued in the thousands of dollars per ounce range would allow countries with large gold reserves, such as the United States, to pay off their national debts by simply selling a small portion of their reserves.

The future will see the high-tech electronic and automotive countries being replaced by the countries capable of massive food production to satisfy growing hunger in the world. When this happens, the human race will have gone full cycle, with gold representing what people want versus what people need. The first gold traded was not for oil, automobiles, electronics, or other physical possessions, but rather was most assuredly traded for food. Although, since that time countries and cultures have fought and been destroyed for the simple possession of gold; it was not the gold that was the cause of the battles, but rather a flaw in the human psychic. If gold had never been discovered, then something else would be in its place of prominence, perhaps diamonds or platinum.

Although the possession of gold has always been the prized possession of kings, another more rare metal was prized more. Ironically, today it is not so rare and is found as one of the most common constituents of the world's garbage. The metal was *aluminum*. Although aluminum is found in one of the most common and abundant minerals in the world which is, aluminum silicates found in granite and clay, no means existed until the 1930's to extract it in its elemental form. It was so rare that only Kings could afford it, and they were mesmerized by how it was the lightest metal which was the opposite of gold which was the heaviest metal. Today we are surrounded by the metal, aluminum. We have aluminum cookware, aluminum cans, aluminum antiperspirants and aluminum is put in the cheese of fast food burgers to enhance the esthetical flow properties. Ironically, there is scientific evidence that suggests that the consumption of aluminum in the human body leads to a host of diseases, such as Alzheimer's disease that did not exist before the introduction of cheap aluminum and which causes an aluminum plaque buildup in the brain.

It therefore was fortuitous that only kings could afford aluminum, as humans tend to consume precious metals both knowingly and unknowingly. For hundreds of years, humans have been consuming gold salts. A popular practice of the American West was the consumption of dissolved gold chloride salts resulting in numerous—and now scientifically provable—medicinal claims. Also, for centuries kings have consumed the precious metal silver, which tended to be dissolved by acidic juices and wines. This caused much of their skin to take on a blue tint; hence royalty was known as *bluebloods*. There was a distinctive health benefit as the element silver is Mother Nature's natural antibiotic. The flu virus dies immediately in the silver goblet used in Catholic churches. The early settlers kept their milk and preserves from going rancid by putting a shiny silver dollar in the bottom of the container. Also, when shot, the early settler would place a silver dollar on the wound before wrapping it up. Colloidal silver—extremely fine silver in a liquid suspension—has been used for centuries to treat bacterial infections, and was in fact used by all medical doctors right up until 1939 when it was displaced by the introduction of penicillin. Unfortunately, a large percentage of the antibiotic drugs that followed are now ineffective against bacterium and viruses, yet the profit-motivated drug industry refuses to return to the use of the now inexpensive and non-patentable precious metal, silver. Perhaps, this is where the expression, *silver bullet against disease*, came from.

If gold had not been discovered, the obvious choice for a metal to replace it would have to be a metal from the rare platinum family of precious metals. Diamonds, which are actually very common and abundant, were only made valuable by advertising design in the 20th century and by the producers holding the majority of production away from the market. Slick marketing slogans, such as "diamonds are forever" and "diamonds are a girl's best friend" have given diamonds a place in human culture. However, since they are abundant, and since they can be made synthetically, the replacement of gold by diamonds would result in a flood of diamonds which would make them worth little.

The obvious choice to replace gold would be the metal platinum, itself. It actually is more rare than gold, is heavier, and possesses more physical attributes than gold. And like gold, platinum cannot be man-made. Unfortunately, platinum and the platinum metals (osmium, iridium, rhodium, rhenium and palladium) are in the same technical no-mans-land that aluminum was in at the turn of the century. The platinum metals tend to form complexes from which they are difficult to extract. The technology does not currently exist to produce enough platinum to replace the appetite for gold possessed by the very rich and the gold vaults of the world. As has been explained in previous chapters, gold is not as uncommon as it is uneconomic to extract. The same is true for the platinum metals. In the future, advances in gold technology may make gold more commonplace, at which time platinum may have to take gold's place of prominence. Until that time comes, man will continue to fight and kill for gold.

Thus, as man learns to use preventive medicine to conquer disease and thereby live longer, his golden years will with no uncertainty be followed by his platinum years, both physically and philosophically.

CHAPTER EIGHT

PLATINUM SCAMS

Platinum was accidentally discovered in the sixteenth century by the Spaniards who did not know what the shiny silver metal was that was contaminating their sluice concentrates from both what is now the state of Texas, and the placers of Columbia. The first description of platinum was made in 1748 by Antonio de Ulloa, a Spanish surveyor. He dubbed the metal "platina" which means "little silver." In Texas at the time, the Spanish typically roasted their ore by layering it sequentially with oily Texas lignite in piles that were surface-sealed with clay and were 60 feet high. They then lit a fire underneath and allowed the stack with oily lignites to smolder for weeks before digging the ore out of the pile and sluicing it to recover the gold and silver. What they had unknowingly done was create a hydrogen (from the oily lignite) reduction furnace (by sealing the pile from air with clay and then burning hydrocarbons). Electric hydrogen reduction furnaces are used by refineries today to reduce platinum into metal.

It should be noted that platinum metal nuggets can be found in certain rare, gold placers and that the Indians of Ecuador made platinum artifacts *long before* the discovery of the Americas by the Europeans. The Spaniards began mining the Columbia placer deposits in 1778 where the platinum to gold ratio was 1:1. This was the world's only source until 1822, when platinum was discovered in the Ural Mountains in Russia, where the platinum to gold ratio was 5:1. Platinum was detected in California placer gold operations in the 1850s, where the platinum to gold ratio was 1:20. In 1885, platinum was discovered in the nickel-copper ores of Sudbury, Ontario, but was not mined until 1919. Platinum was discovered in South Africa in 1890 but was also not mined until 1925. Platinum was discovered in the Tulameen deposits in British Columbia where the platinum to gold ratio was 1:2. The Tulameen river itself had a platinum to gold ratio of 1:10. The major U.S. lode deposit is located in the Stillwater complex in Montana. Today, 98% of all platinum metals are produced from lode deposits in Canada, South Africa and Russia.

Platinum ranks with gold in value. Some of the platinum metals, such as rhodium, are far more valuable. As such they have always been sought by miners. The major source has been found in sluice boxes in specific regions of the world, such as the Tulameen river in Canada and the Volga river in Russia. In South Africa, platinum it has been found and mined in kimberlite pipes. Because of their rareness and because of their unique physical properties, the platinum group metals (consisting of platinum, iridium, osmium, ruthenium, rhodium, and palladium) are very difficult to analyze accurately. The platinum group metals all have very high densities and are all resistant to oxidation and to reaction with most chemicals. They all also melt at high temperatures (several times higher than the temperatures used to assay gold), and they boil substantially higher than the temperatures generated by arc emission spectrographs. What this means is, unlike gold, they cannot be collected by the assayers' lead and they cannot be analysed by the chemists' spectrograph. Despite this, there are millions of analyses reported every year, and of course the "*expert*" doing the analysis swear to the accuracy. In reality, the platinums can only be assayed using a rare copper sulfide fusion procedure for which only a handful of refinery technicians are trained.

By far the main use of platinum today is as an automotive and chemical catalyst. A catalyst is a substance that speeds up reaction rates often a million fold or more. One of its most valuable features is that it is used in very tiny amounts, usually parts-per-million. Despite these small amounts, over 700,000 troy ounces were used by U.S. industry each year in the 1990s, equaling about 75% of the total production. Platinum is also used by the pharmaceutical industry for numerous medicines and the agricultural industry in fertilizers. Other major uses are related to their unique properties, chemical inertness, high melting point, electrical conductivity, and pleasing appearance.

As a result of the extreme difficulty in assaying the platinum group of metals, there are always thousands of groups in America that believe with all their heart that they are the exception and that they have discovered a high grade platinum mine. These groups have never, nor will they ever, produce one ounce of platinum, although many will succeed in producing metal which they swear are *platinoids*. Whenever these metals are weighed and their volume is measured by water displacement, the resulting specific gravity or density is in the five to seven range. The platinums are many times this. When presented with this physical impossibility, they usually respond with spectrographic analysis done by some inexperienced professor who did not know that the platinums had to be physically excited to give off a light spectrum and that his spectrograph did not reach the required high temperature. More commonly, the response is an assay report from one of the thousands of uncertified laboratories. A certified laboratory usually provides assays at a fraction of the price and follows specific procedures approved by the industry and government. Despite this, even though their analysis is more often correct than the uncertified laboratory, their assays are not always correct. This will be disputed as all laboratories have *pedigreed experts* that will dispute this claim. This causes mass public confusion and allows the proliferation of numerous platinum scams.

The way that the average person can sort out the assay mess is to purchase powdered platinum metals from a refinery, such as Johnson Matthey, and then put small measured amounts into the ore in question prior to submitting the sample for assay. One can also run a blank, which is a sample which cannot contain the metal being assayed—ashtray sand or your wife's plant soil, for example. You will be surprised how often the latter two assay several thousand dollars in platinums and just as how often the country's best laboratories cannot find the store bought platinums that you injected into the samples. Even the refineries can fail this test. In the end, you can trust no laboratory analysis and will discover that the only accurate platinum assay is the refinery receipt which you attained by selling the metal, and remember that this is rarely done as none of the thousands of platinum prospect groups has ever been paid for an ounce of platinum. Thus, the best advice for the average person is the same advice for the expert: keep your money in your wife's purse.

Now for those with technical curiosity, Ledoux and Company of Teaneck, New Jersey, is the platinum "Assay Umpire" for the major refineries of the world. A recent publication by Ledoux and company entitled, *"Applications of the Copper Sulfide Collecting System"* gives some insight into the problem of platinum assaying. In summary, it says that the lead collection systems, used by certified laboratories, are incapable of recovering the platinums. It states that without large amounts of gold and silver added to the assay charge, platinum and palladium will not be collected in the assayer's bead. It also states that rhodium, ruthenium, and iridium do not alloy with the assayer's inquarted silver (silver metal added to the assay charge). This is supported by the most respected assay manual, *Shepard and Dietrich,* which further states, "the cupellation process is subject to (1) loss of precious metals by volatilization, and (2) absorption or loss of precious metals that enter the body of the cupel (the bone cup used to absorb the molten lead produced from the assay leaving the gold and silver on its surface)" (page 230). Even *Compton's Interactive*

Encyclopedia, in its section on assaying, states that "osmium and ruthenium are largely lost during cupellation."

Thus, it is not unusual to find that the assay *experts* who are always so certain that they are correct, are incapable of assaying the store-bought platinums which you inject into your samples. For these reasons, and many more, the internationally recognized father of platinum analyses, Professor F. E. Beamish, in his book, *The Analytical Chemistry of Noble Metals* states that *"despite more than a century of analytical effort, no procedure has been recorded that can be used with confidence for the direct determination of each of the noble metals in primary deposits"* (page 363). Professor Beamish states that *"the platinum metals are rare in nature and in general cannot be determined or often detected directly in naturally occurring ores" (*page 491). He also warns that *"an apparent deficiency of the classical fire assay is that the lead collector is alien to the precious metals"* (page 492). Professor Beamish personally told the author of this book that it would take two solid years of his time to accurately analyze just one of the platinum metals in an unknown ore, and that the procedure developed would probably only work on that one ore. He also advised that no one should ever attempt to evaluate platinum metals in an ore without close consultation with a world-accepted analytical authority. This is almost never done by the thousands of groups chasing the platinum dream.

Dr. Tom Holmen, who has 157 research patents and is a former precious metal researcher for the American Space Agency, stated that "other than Professor Beamish, only a few people in the precious metal refineries and their few consulting experts are capable of assaying the precious metal in ores". With Dr. Holmen, the author succeeded in removing compounds in ores that were inhibiting the detection of contained precious metals, and International Nickel—a platinum producer—then analyzed substantial amounts of precious metal in the treated ore and only trace amounts in the untreated ore.

In laboratory experiments, the author was able to make store bought platinums *disappear* from analytical detection. Professor Anthony Beard, former Chief Metallurgist for Englehard stated that he had shared the same experience while processing precious metals in his refinery.

In other laboratory experiments, the author was able to produce a saleable platinum metal product—according to the Mitsubitsi Corporation—produced from the sodium amalgamation of sluice box concentrates which had been roasted with coal oil, similar to Texas lignite.

Dr. Murel Goddell, former head of Metals Research at the Colorado School of Mines and former metal researcher for the world's largest platinum producer, Anglo Corporation in South Africa, states that outside of the Platinum Cartel, there are less than a handful of people who know anything about platinum assaying. Dr. Goddell included the author in the handful, but the author's response was that what he did know about platinum assaying were the thousands of things he knew must exist but of which he was ignorant.

Dr. R. C. Bovrell, Technical Director of Impala Platinum Ltd., one of South Africa's leading platinum producers, writes "To our knowledge, *there are no commercial laboratories in this country that can do reliable platinum analyses.*"

For the thousands of platinum *"experts"* who do not heed professor Beamish's, Dr. Holmen's, Dr. Goddell's and Dr. Bovell's caution that *"no assay procedure for the precious metals can be used with confidence."* I leave you with a quote from A.J. Daniel (American novelist, 1921 - 1982):

> *"Being stupid isn't knowing much,*
> *Nor is it wanting to know much,*
> *Being stupid is believing you know enough."*

CHAPTER NINE

GOLD SCAMS

Unfortunately, for every platinum scam, there must be 100 gold scams. The majority of victims of gold scams are usually people who truly believe in the project. The other 2% usually make their money from sources that are not obvious. For example, one particular scam was executed three times on a placer gold property in Rich Hill, Arizona. Each time that the project was doomed to fail (usually due to a lack of gold in the ore), the production equipment was sold 5 cents to the dollar. Then, when the project was revived with a new group of investors, the equipment was made available with a 20 % savings to the investor at just 80 cents to the dollar. The project soon became doomed, and the process was repeated again. The historical, huge potato size nuggets had mesmerized each new set of investors. The real gold mine, however, was in the equipment used to process the ore.

One of the investors of the last Rich Hill Gold Project asked the author to investigate whether any fraud had occurred in the project. The author made arrangements to meet with the mine manager of the project. Three days prior to showing up on the property, the author visited the regional Department of Mineral Resources, as every state has a geological agency that monitors mining activity and keeps public records. Collecting the geological and mining information on the property was routine. However, while doing so, the author happened to hear a conversation between two gentlemen discussing another mining property. It was obvious that they were amateurs and that they were about to be parted from their money. They turned out to be the regional director of the FBI and an IRS prosecuting attorney. They were given a brief tutorial by the author and responded by providing information on the Rich Hill Project. Apparently, they had suspected that only a portion of the money raised for the project "went into the ground" to become tax deductible. After a three-day onsite inspection of the property, the assay laboratory and analyses, and the mined ore deposit, the author calculated that $1,300,000 had been spent on the project, which included the equipment rip off. As $5,000,000 had been raised for the project, that left $3,700,000, which was the exact amount that two of the operators had used to purchase a South American airline that was later traded for Swiss real estate. The IRS was ecstatic, as the project turned out to be an unsuccessful *tax fraud gold mine*.

Of course, history has taught us that the most famous gold con is the bait and switch routine, and although initially used to successfully steal most of the gold mines from the Indians, it is still a popular tool today to use against the white man. Intelligence has nothing to do with the success of the scam; it is based on simple human trust. Whenever miners are successful in producing large quantities of nugget gold, there is never any problem selling their production. The idea is to always sell to the highest bidder. If given the time, one could travel to Europe and sell large nuggets to jewelers for more than 125% their weight in gold. Now, this is an excellent price as most of the buyers only pay about 90%, which is the average gold content of nuggets. This was the basis for one of the best gold scams ever perpetrated and was successfully done on the author in the early 1980's. Just as the production of large quantities of Yukon nugget gold began, the author was approached by a well-dressed and well-groomed gentleman who offered to pay cash on receipt for 100% of the weight of the nuggets, which was 10% more than usual. The gentleman called himself Professor

Gordon Briggs from McGill University in Montreal. He claimed to be a gold expert who had a market for the nuggets in Europe at 125%. Everyone would make a lot of money. True to his word, he showed up on the site and paid for the first shipment of gold in new, crisp $1,000 bills, which he slowly, and loudly, counted out, one at a time. This became a common routine over the short operating season in the Yukon. Then, on the second to last shipment, Professor Briggs showed up on the site to take his nugget shipment, but, as he explained, did not have time to make it to the bank to get cash. He offered a check which of course was declined. He then offered to accompany anyone to the bank, and to not receive the nugget supply until the check was cashed. This seemed reasonable, and in the end the check was processed by tellers who treated Professor Briggs like royalty.

Then came the last and largest cleanup of the placer season. Professor Briggs, claiming to have vehicle problems and could not make it to the site asked that the gold be brought to town where he would pick it up a few days later. The request from our trusted friend was complied with. The day came and no Professor Briggs. Then, late that night, Professor Briggs phoned to say that he would be flying in for a one hour stopover before proceeding to Europe. True to his word he showed up precisely on time, only without any cash. However, it was Sunday and no banks were open. He offered to miss his flight and stay over until Monday to cash his check, or to return two weeks later with the cash. As the cash was needed before that and because we had found his checks to be good in the past, we hurried him on his way with his non refundable airline ticket and our gold. The check bounced on Monday. *We had been conned!*

But the con perpetrated on us was tiny compared to the real con for which Professor Briggs used our gold. According to Interpol, Professor Briggs had successfully carried out a con on over 72 "wealthy women" and had robbed them of millions of dollars. After he had made the deal to buy our nuggets, Professor Briggs, with his charm and his well manicured goatee and mustache, approached the 72 women individually and told each of them he had a legitimate proposition that could see them make 15 % on their money in less than five days. He would simply buy their nuggets for 100% of the weighted value, as stated in our contract which he showed them, and then proceed to Europe where his buyers would pay him 125% or more. He would then return and split the profit with each of them. Initially he cautioned his victims not to invest too much money in the scheme until they saw how well it worked. He took their money and attained crisp new $1,000 bills from the bank to set up his con for the miners. When he got his first shipment of nuggets, he took it to each of his victims and spread it out on their coffee tables. There was more gold than their money could buy, he explained how he had to get a couple of his *male friends* to help him. Once the victims had examined and fingered the nuggets and were mesmerized, he proceeded to Europe and sold them. When he returned he went to each of the women to show them the money made, which he had in crisp new $1,000 bills. He offered to return their investment with the profit earned, or they could *"let it ride."* Most of the women not only let it ride, but increased their investment so that he would not have to get any more money from his "male friends." This routine was repeated on one-week intervals all summer long, until just before the last cleanup of gold, which he explained would cost him more, so he needed a little extra money. He took our gold worth a few hundred thousand dollars, he took their money by the millions, and was never seen again.

Interpol was watching for Professor Briggs, who used the alias of Ian McCleod from Inland Seafood out of Denver, to show up in the European jewelry market, but instead, he went south to see a friend of mine in Phoenix who owned a gold refinery. To the dismay of the refinery, he had all of the nuggets smelted and paid by a check which bounced. They later reported seeing him on a Los Angeles television program where he was sitting behind his bars of bullion claiming to be a *"renowned gold expert."* He was undoubtedly in the middle of his next gold scam. The call to the police proved fruitless as the show had been previously recorded. I received numerous calls from his victims, not all of whom were little old ladies. One was a young and beautiful stewardess who had met Professor Briggs on a flight to San Francisco. That night after he had shown her a suitcase full of gold nuggets and then wined and dined her, she decided to mortgage her house and join her new boyfriend in his venture. Minutes after getting the her mortgage money, he disappeared for good. She told me that she found out later that other stewardesses had fallen for the same scheme.

A few years later I was in the Braniff Club in the Denver airport when I heard an announcement: "Would Ian McCleod go to a white courtesy phone." With my heart pounding loudly, I leaped to my feet and by leaning over a railing on the second floor, I could see Professor Briggs talking on a courtesy phone. Once again an emmergency call to the police proved to be too late, as I later watched the police dust the phone for his fingerprints.

Billionaires and gold scams are an unheard of combination. That's because billionaires have enough money to surround themselves with expertise. However, selling a billionaire interest in a legitimate gold play is often done. On one particular occasion, because of our experience in the gold industry, we were asked by a Texas billionaire, who said "call me Bum," to come to Texas for discussions. A very professional and reputable geologist heard of Bum's offer and asked if he could accompany us, as he had a very rich mine which would be of interest to all parties. Once in the conference, our geologist commanded the floor, extolling the merits of his mine, which had initially been mined as a mercury mine but also contained substantial gold. It sounded fantastic! Then, after he was courteously asked to leave, we were subjected to intense questioning by some of the world's leading gold experts. The next day in Bum's office, we were told that we had passed the test and we were offered a lot of money for all of our assets, as long as Bum ended up owning the majority of it. We responded that *we were not for sale*, and have many times regretted this rash reaction. Bum smiled and then asked me to examine a piece of highgrade ore that he had in his office. When asked where the ore came from, he replied, "from the mine your geologist tried to sell me. You see, I have owned that mine for two years. If I had told your geologist that I wanted *his mine,* he would have gone and tried to swindle it from the owner." This type of scam, where experts claim to *own* or *know of* an ore deposit, usually means that they have no ownership in the property. Also, even though a few may actually own the property, the property usually has so many skeletons in the closet (people who will make claims of ownership once value has been established), that it is worthless.

All in all, most gold scams are successful because the lure for gold causes the average person to become mesmerized. The banker who readily signs a $250,000 loan becomes giddy and mesmerized when only $10,000 worth of gold nuggets are placed in his hands. How could so little be worth so much? A much better question should be asked, and that is "How could so much money be spent on so little gold?" Remember 99 out of every 100 gold prospects loses money. The only question that a prospective gold investor should ask is *"Why?"*

The number one answer is that, although the assay of the sample is usually accurate, the *sample itself did not represent the ore fed* to the mill. This can happen for a number of reasons. The most common reason is mining dilution of the ore. The gold ore has to be blasted out with dynamite. Unfortunately, most of the time a large amount of unconsolidated wall rock falls in with the blasted ore, causing substantial dilution. Other times the ore ribbons become thinner and thicker in intervals and it must be mined to a minimum thickness resulting in substantial dilution.

Another reason that the sample did not represent mill feed is the *nugget effect.* This can best be explained by placing a one ounce nugget in a one-ton pile of sand making the sand one ounce of gold per ton. If the grade of the sand, is assessed by assaying (29 grams of sample are used for a fire assay) then all of the assays will be 0.000 oz/ton except one which will be 30,000 oz/ton. Thus if the whole pile is assayed, 30,000 assays will be 0.000 oz/ton and only one will be 30,000 oz/ton. If half the pile is assayed and the nugget is in one, then 15,000 will be 0.000 oz/ton and one will be 30,000 oz/ton, and thus the average would be 2.000 oz/ton which we know is incorrect. If the nugget does not show up in these assays, then we would conclude, incorrectly, that the average assay is 0.000 oz/ton. Also if we assay one tenth of the pile and one has the nugget in it, the average assay would be 10.000 oz/ton which would also be incorrect. Thus the only way to assay the ore accurately when large pieces of gold are contained is to assay 100% of the ore, which of course is never done. Unfortunately, when coarse gold is contained in the ore, the assessment by assay is usually substantially higher than the mill feed. It is unfortunate because everyone desperately wants to believe there is higher grades of gold in the ore. Most gold mines fail for this reason.

Of course, sometimes the ore samples are intentionally or unintentionally high-graded (the highest visible grade is sampled as representative). This is done by those incompetent or by those who *"know"* that if the mine would "just start up, the high pockets of rich ore would be found" to make the mine successful. This of, course, almost never happens.

What should the layperson considering investing in gold know before parting with his money? *First*, that historically 99 out of 100 investors lose money. This means that the gold experts giving the advice are almost always wrong. *Second*, ask "was the ore assessment done by third-party professionals?" This is a must! *Third*, ask "were all of the assays done by government-certified labs?" The assays may not always be accurate, but in the history of mining, there has never been an economically successful gold mine based on uncertified assays, and the odds are less than one in a million that you will be the first. *Fourth*, when looking at the grade of the mill feed, if there is coarse gold in the ore, the assays may be anonymously high due to the nugget effect. *Fifth*, when looking at the ore reserves, how much money was spent? It costs about $1.00 per ton to assess a placer gold prospect and at least $10.00 per ton to assess a hard rock gold ore. Thus the 100 million tons of placer gold ore would require $100 million in exploration expenditures, and usually claims of having such large amounts of ore are based on expenditures of less than $10,000.

Also prospective investors should be watching for "red flags." The word *"platinoid"* is often used by scam artists. If you are asked to invest in "drums of concentrates" stored in warehouses in such places as Las Vegas, run don't walk. Millions in cash and real estate have been lost on these concentrates, most of which do not exist, and those that do are over-valued one hundred fold. Another red flag is "the gold and platinums *are tied up in the black sands* making it impossible to assay." This is a half-truth, as gold is easily assayed but usually uneconomical to extract, and, of course, the platinums which 99% of the time are not in the black sands in economic amounts, are indeed almost impossible to assay. Another red flag to watch for is "if there is only 10% of the gold that the assays indicate, we will still make millions of dollars." Almost 100% of the time, the amount of gold actually present is *less than 1% of what the assays indicate*, meaning that you have already lost.

Prospective gold investors should also be aware of the 10 golden rules:

1) *The answer to "What will go wrong?", is "Everything !"*
2) *Even when you win you lose.*
3) *The man who has the gold makes the rules.*
4) *God put gold where only a fool would set foot.*
5) *You can't eat it.*
6) *You can't drink it.*
7) *You can't take it with you.*
8) *Gold almost always costs more than you get paid for it.*
9) *The chance you will lose your money is 100 to 1.*
10) *Those who steal gold die poor.*

CHAPTER TEN

THE RECOVERY OF ASSAYABLE INVISIBLE GOLD

There are two kinds of invisible gold, one where the gold is too small for the human eye to detect, and one where analytical problems make it difficult to assay. The latter will be discussed in detail in the next two chapters. Many professional publications demonstrate that gold assays suffer from the same industrial doubts that are cast on platinum assays. For example Claudia Gasparrini's article *"Fire Assay: Its Potential and Its Limitations"* published in the July 1993 issue of Mining magazine. Gasparrini states "Problems associated with the production of correct fire assays do exist: they are evidently complex and far from understood." and she further states "the examples of high recovery rates, in some cases more than 100% of the assay (which is impossible if the assays are correct) indicate that there indeed can be inaccuracies."

Also, geologist J. P. Sawyer in *Special Publication No. 63* of the Geological Society Publishing House, England states,

"Some of the classical analytical methods in standard use today, such as fire assay, are not capable of providing an easy universal solution to the determination of all naturally occurring ores." Sawyer further states "What is needed is an *open-minded* critical monitoring of all analytical procedures and a move away from blind acceptance of analytical results purely on the basis of what has become standard practice in the industry."

In 1976, Marcel Valee, Chief Development Geologist, Soquem, presented a paper to the Canadian Institute of Mining in which he states, "The observed *variability of repeated gold assays*, as well as discontinuities in the frequency distribution of the sample population, led to a program of investigation of sampling errors contributing to gold assay variability. A survey showed *significant differences* in the sampling procedures of 8 certified laboratories. We feel that assayers, geologists, mining and milling personnel in the mineral industry still have not paid enough attention to the implications of sampling theory into their work." In other words, what good is it if the assay on the 29.2 grams of assay sample is totally accurate, when the assay sample does not represent the ore being evaluated because of sampling errors by the geologist, miners, millers and assayers.

All of these professional criticisms and numerous other criticisms of the accuracy of gold ore assessments are summarily dismissed by the *"gold experts,"* most of whom have no assay experience, and those that do, have a bias to justify their services, in addition to not wanting to be sued for the incorrect analysis. It is also interesting that most of these experts are good at spending the money, but have never had to pay the bills out of their own pockets. In addition, the errors are quite frequently repeated by the same individual or others resulting in the *duplication* of inaccuracies. When lies or errors are repeated often enough, they soon come to be regarded as *"the truth."* Lord, help us all !

Despite the fact that mining journals and assay text books discuss potential inaccuracies in the analysis of gold, on the whole and unlike the platinum group of metals, *"most"* certified gold assays are a correct assessment of the sample being analyzed. Assays of ore samples with free-milling exposed gold are especially accurate. In these samples, the gold could take the form of nugget gold found in placers or rich quartz ore veins, or crystal gold found attached to the minerals deep within the earth or unattached in surface alluvials. The recovery of the nugget gold may seem apparently easy, however, recovery efficiencies are almost shameful.

These efficiencies have not only been evaluated by assay assessment of the ore tailings (tailings are the ore after it has been processed to remove the gold), but also by *re-processing* the tailings and measuring the gold recovered. The early miners in Alaska and California would sometimes extend their normally 25 foot sluice boxes, which is the average length used today, to up to one mile long. Although the initial 25 foot section was constantly cleaned out, the mile long sections were only cleaned out once a year. The gold recovered in the longer section demonstrated that the 25 foot initial section of sluice recovered only about *18% of the total gold*, while the first 200 feet recovered *50% of the total gold*. The problem with sluicing the gold is that if the sluice boxes are not frequently cleaned out, they pack off with dense material, and the recovery drops dramatically. Therefore the current compromise length is 25 feet with a recovery of 18%. On the other hand, the free milling gold from a *high grade* ore deposit is not recovered by sluicing, but rather by a host of other and more efficient gravity systems such as gravity tables which slowly collect gold sliding across a tilted table at a slower rate than the less dense ore, and jigs which vibrate the gold to the bottom of a container allowing the less dense ore to spill over the top.

In the case of the *crystalline gold* attached to minerals and unattached in alluvials (this gold is usually referred to as micron gold), there have been thousands of *unsuccessful* attempts to use the inexpensive gravity systems to recover the gold. They usually fail as the gold attached mineral is only a fraction as dense as the gold, and also when attached to sulfides, which it usually is, it even has the tendency to float. Even in the rare cases when gravity recoveries are successful, the problem of separating the gold from the attached mineral still exists. Without doubt, the most successful process for the recovery of micron gold is the use of cyanide. To the layperson, who knows that cyanide gas is used in the death chamber, the process seems both dangerous and environmentally unfriendly. History shows that just the opposite is true.

No miner using cyanide over the past 100 years has ever been killed. Also, once the cyanide has been exposed to air, say by flowing down one mile of a creek, it is chemically converted into a harmless substance. Although the public should be vigilant, there is not much danger that anyone will ever be injured by the cyanide used in North America. Unfortunately, this is not true in third world developing countries where mining regulations are lax, and where mining companies take dangerous chances to save money. Faulty dykes have burst, spewing millions of gallons of active cyanide into populated rivers. Thus, even though the use of cyanide has proven to be safe in North America, the world would be better off if the cyanide system were replaced. *But with what?*

CHAPTER ELEVEN

A NEW APPROACH TO THE RECOVERY
OF INVISIBLE GOLD

Back in the early 1960s when electron microscopes became available to the analytical industry, very few could afford them. By the late 1970s the cost of electron microscopes had dropped to the point where even the author frequently used one. One day while examining sluice box concentrates, a series of 18 micron octahedral crystals (looked like two pyramids stacked base to base) were seen in the cracks, crevices and ledges of large, cubic magnetite crystals. When the question was asked "are these micron octahedral crystals gold?" the response from the *"experts"* was laughter. If not gold, then what were they? An experiment was devised to find out.

A 1927 Russian experiment discovered that if mercury was electrified, the amalgamation of gold would occur at *"1000 times the normal rate."* Thus, by electrifying the mercury negative in the bottom of a beaker, and then inserting a positive probe in the swirling slurry over top of the mercury, a high speed electro-amalgamation was induced. Quickly dissolving the mercury in nitric acid liberated the contained gold, 18 micron octahedral gold crystals. Other, non-free milling gold ores were electro-amalgamated, resulting in the same 18 micron octahedral crystals. In many cases the octahedral crystals could be seen, using the electron microscope, adhering in the crevices of pyrite crystals. It was believed that the source of the invisible micron gold, that had previously only be extracted by cyanide, had been identified.

Now that we knew the size and the shape of the invisible gold crystals, how, without the use of cyanide, could they be extracted from the ore in which they were contained? The first obvious conclusion was that no variation of any existing gravity system, sluice, jig or table, would ever be able to detach or recover these crystals. We knew that electro-amalgamation in a beaker worked, so initially most of the research was pointed in this direction.

First, beakers obviously could not be used industrially. What was needed was a flow-through system. Since mercury has a density of 13, it would be impossible to flow a slurry down through it. Thus, it was obvious that the positively charged slurry would have to be flowed *up* through the negatively charged mercury. Initially everyone thought that the mercury losses would be great, and they were until it was realized that the negatively charged mercury would respond to other charged fields. Thus negatively charged screens were placed above the slurry and with experimentation, measuring the height of the *mercury shower* as clean water flowed through it and the electrical charge of the upper screens were varied, it was found that a negative electrical charge of over 150 DC volts could suppress the negatively charged mercury shower to one third its size and dramatically reduce mercury loss.

The final design for this amalgamator trap, or Amtrap, was a four inch square, 16 inch high plastic reservoir with a 45 degree tapered bottom with a one inch inlet tube inserted about 3 inches up. The mercury was filled above the tube so that when water flowed it created a shower of mercury that filled the container. The tapered bottom allowed the heavier gold amalgams to drop to the bottom crevice where they entered a rubber tube and could be collected. A cylindrical wire mesh screen, 10 inches high and 4 inches in diameter was electrically charged negative and inserted into the mercury. This kept the mercury charged and repelled the mercury shower to the center of the container where the ore was flowing. It also provided calm areas in the corners where entrapped mercury could drop back into the reservoir. The upper outlet was also a one inch tube which meant that the rate of flow of the slurry was reduced sixteen fold while in the container. As the ore slurry was previously charged positive prior to entering the container, the positively charged gold would make contact with a negatively charged ball of mercury, electrons would exchange resulting in an ***instantaneous electroamalgamation***.

Tests of ores containing free milling gold resulted in almost perfect recoveries. Each four inch Amtrap could effectively process 1000 pounds of ore per hour. Usually 4 Amtraps were run in parallel 16 inches square, and the capacity was 4,000 pounds per hour or 48 tons per day. Two of these tiny units could replace a huge 100 ton per day gold mill facility. Also, the size of the gold was irrelevant as all micron gold was captured. The Amtrap was the first development since cyanide that was capable of economically recovering fine gold.

Despite the minute amount of mercury lost, any use of mercury was frowned on by the government. Also, the gold bound to pyrite and magnetite (octahedral gold is positively charged on its surface by structure and both pyrite and magnetite are negatively charged on their surfaces which cause them to be bound together by electric charge) was not recoverable by electroamalgamation. Another process had to be developed.

Famous hydrogeologist, Hjulstrom, after measuring the depositional patterns of thousands of deltas all over the world, developed a pattern for the prediction of deposition based on velocity of the water (centimeters per second) and size of the particles (diameter in millimeters). The resultant Hjulstrom's

Diagram has been used by thousands of sedimentologists for over 60 years and is considered to exemplify the laws of physics. Hjulstrom based his deposition (dropping out of a moving slurry to come to rest on the bottom of a sediment) on the average density of quartz, 2.5, and the distance over which the deposition occurs being 100 meters (or 110 yards). His diagram is the velocity of the slurry versus size of the particle in the slurry. The diagram is proportioned to show *erosion, transport and deposition.* (see diagram.)

DIAGRAM #1 Hjulstrom's Diagram With 18 Micron Quartz and Gold Plotted at Various G-Forces

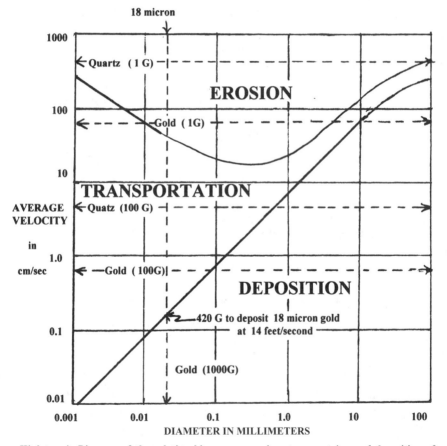

Hjulstrom's Diagram of the relationship among erosion, transportaion and deposition of sedimentary particles. *"Recent Marine Sediments"* American Association Petroleum Geol 1939

From Hjulstrom's diagram it can readily be seen that quartz, up to 100 millimeters (about 4 inches) in diameter, moving at 10 miles per hour or 445 centimeters per second (the velocity of water in a sluice box) will remain in the erosion phase. Gold, a size of 6 millimeters (about one quarter inch), which is also 7.7 times as dense as quartz, will drop out of the slurry which is exactly what happens in the sluice box. The average invisible gold, at 18 microns will always remain in the erosion phase when only the force of gravity, 1 G, is applied. Therefore it would be *physically impossible to catch micron gold in a sluice box*. The 18 micron size intersects the depositional phase at 0.2 cm/sec., which is 420 times slower in velocity than gold travelling at 1G. Therefore, 420 Gs of force over 100 meters would be required to deposit micron gold from a moving slurry. What all this means is that no conventional system or rearrangement of conventional systems could even come remotely close to succeeding in catching 18 micron gold. Despite this no-win situation, almost all gold "experts" continue to try. As a matter of fact, since most systems are no larger than 25 feet, the implication from Hjulstorm's diagram is that thousands of Gs of force would be required. A force other than gravity would, therefore, according to the laws of physics as demonstrated by Hjulstrom's diagram, have to be employed.

According to the laws of physics, only one other force seemed possible, and that was electrical force. A simple demonstration of electrical force that is shown in high schools, is the lifting of a piece of cigarette ash with a charged piece of glass. The ash is light and the charge is small, but the experiment demonstrates a force that behaves according to formula. These formulas calculate that in order to put a thousand Gs of force on an 18 micron piece of gold, hundreds of thousands of volts "applied over one inch" would be required. Initial experimentation recovering gold using high voltages demonstrated that the formulas were accurate, but resulted in several electrocutions. It was obvious that such high voltages could not be safely used. Further experimentation showed that no shocks were produced if the voltage did not rise above 10 volts. Thus, for safety reasons the testing voltage was set at "1 volt." But, this provides only *0.02 Gs of force* over 1 inch. However, it could be calculated that, 1 volt could also produce *20 Gs* if the distance were reduced to one millimeter (0.04 inches), and also produce *1000 G's* if the distance were reduced to 0.1 millimeter. This meant that if electrical force was to be used, the positively electrically charged 18 micron gold particle would have to approach within 0.1 millimeters (or .0.004 inches) of the opposite negatively charged collector, and do it in a turbulent 10 miles per hour slurry. Although this may seem impossible at first, the *"parameters for success"* had been set.

The first consideration to forcing the gold close to the collector was cyclones. At 10 miles per hour, a 4 inch cyclone produces 4 Gs of force; a 2 inch cyclone produces 16 Gs; a 1 inch cyclone produces 64 Gs and a 0.5 inch cyclone produces 256 Gs. Obviously, 0.5 inch cyclones would be required, *thousands of them*, and they would have to process the large one-quarter inch ore in a slurry. This, of course, would be impossible. However, it was realized that conventional cyclones were not the only way to produce high G forces. All that is required is a 0.5 inch water swirl moving at 10 miles per hour and this could be accomplished by directing the water slurry stream at a critical angle into 0.5 inch square cells. The slurry going in would have to *"swirl out"* if the angle of entry were correct. The concept seemed simple enough, and experimentation began.

One-half inch plastic squares were designed and a standard ore was prepared to test each design. Invisible gold was blended in 25 tons of ore so that the final grade was 0.100 oz/ton. Recovery with a standard sluice box would be less than 1%, but with the very first design of arrayed cells, the recovery was an impressive 5%. This success was short lived, as all other designs were also in the 5% range. One "long shot" design change resulted in the recovery going to 17%, but without any explanation. Further experiments gave worse results. Then one day, we realized that one of Mother Nature's specific rules is that *"most movement is cyclic."*

The lights went on, or rather, ***the lights were turned off***. A strobe light (a light that turns on and off at preset intervals) was turned on and the frequency was adjusted in the dark while the slurry was run. Then, at about 72 cycles per second, the water appeared to stop and hang in suspension over some cells. Twenty-seven water drops could be counted coming out of over 5,000 cells. This was at the 5% gold recovery rate. At the 17% gold recovery rate, 92 water drops could be counted. Over the next four months, with the guidance of the strobe light, the number of water drops gradually rose to 3,500 out of 5,000, at which the recovery of gold was 97%. That meant that the gold could be recovered with 70% of the cells swirling, 30 % were not functional due to large particle deflection. One secret was that the cells had to be slightly tapered inwards.

Processing regular ores resulted in the same high recovery. The 3,500 high force mini-swirls with a one-third inch stream of slurry created almost 300 Gs which was applied to the gold which only had to be moved about one eighth of an inch to get closer than 0.1 millimeter which allowed the electric force to apply thousands of Gs to the gold, thereby entrapping it. The rate of processing with this process, described as the ***Differential Charge Recovery System (DCRS)*** was about 40 tons per hour of throughput or 1,000 tons per day. No chemicals were used and the system recovered micron gold that previously could only be recovered with cyanide.

Unfortunately, to prove the system works to the world, a successful operation would be required. This is unfortunate because 99% of gold projects fail because of lack of gold, and to find a successful project requires an enormous amount of money. Because the technology of differential charging ores in a slurry was so new with no one in the world doing anything remotely similar, and because that meant that there were probably thousands of unknown parameters involved, a patent was not applied for immediately. Eager investors, most of whom ***had all the answers***, were brought in to expedite the project. The next ten years were filled with joy as the field experiments were mostly successful, and disappointment as the almost always impossible exploration projects failed. Each time the *"technology"* was questioned. But every time the DCRS system was tested against known gold content ores, the system was successful. Also, invisible gold added to the ore was always recovered. For example, when it appeared that differential charging may not be recovering the gold from the thick, mucky, lead/zinc tailings of Hudson Bay Mining and Smelting's Flin Flon mill, fine gold was added to the slurry. The recovery was excellent. The mill *"later concluded"* by assays which are always days after the fact, that the grade of gold had indeed dropped off, and that there had been no gold to recover.

Ironically, each time that the technology was questioned (because it failed to recover the gold that was *"thought"* to be in the sample), a size analysis of the gold that was recovered, obtained by physically screening the recovered gold, showed that the majority of the gold was the rarely seen fine to invisible. For placer gold tests, more then 75% was less than 80 mesh (less than 0.007 inches), and for hard rock gold tests, more than 75% was less than 300 mesh (less than 0.001 inches). What makes the recovery of such fine gold ironical is the fact that no conventional gravity system can recover any significant amount of gold in these small size ranges. Despite this fact, geological and metallurgical professionals had no other explanation than to dismiss the DCRS process because it did not recover the amount of gold that they *"thought"* was in the ore. They would say that "The equipment doesn't work." Of course, more detailed evaluation of theses ores proved that their initial evaluations had been wrong, and for all of the same reasons why experts are historically wrong more than 99% of the time. The gold just wasn't present in the amounts that they had calculated, and that was why the certified assays of their tailings samples virtually showed almost no gold present (no gold in the tailings combined with gold recovered in hand means that all of the gold had been recovered by the DCRS process). However, the doubt cast by their initial evaluations meant that substantial more experimentation was needed to disperse all doubts. Thus, the technology development prior to patenting required ten years. This development will be described in the next chapter.

CHAPTER TWELVE

THE DEVELOPMENT OF THE DIFFERENTIAL CHARGE RECOVERY SYSTEM, (DCRS)

The year was 1979, and the first opportunity to test the new differential charge recovery system (DCRS) presented itself. A substantial amount of low grade ore, mined but not processed, was acquired at Beresford, Manitoba. Eager investors, with gold in their eyes, lined up to participate in the building of a gold mill to pulverize the ore and employ the new DCRS gold extraction technology. Wow! It was exciting! Nothing short of a hurricane or earthquake could prevent the success of the new process, and both of these don't exist in Beresford, Manitoba. The mill was built in the wilds with bears roaming through the camp. First the water flow system was tested, and then the ore crushing system was tested. Once debugged, the ore was then slowly put through the DCRS system for a few hours. Initial indications looked exciting. It was decided that the crew would spend the weekend in town relaxing before startup on Monday. We had succeeded and it was time to celebrate. What could go wrong?

Sunday morning we woke up to a monsoon storm. By early Monday morning, the storm was still raging as we started out for the mine. The bridge in the town was almost submerged by the cresting river. We proceeded on up the river road at a very slow pace. The river seemed to be getting deeper and much, much wider. As we rounded our last turn, the river, usually about 80 feet wide, had crested to about 1,000 feet wide, and there was a very large object slowly floating downstream. There were gasps of horror as we realized that *the object was our mill!*

Ok, so we were unprepared for the 50 year flood. But it could never happen again, at least not for another 50 years. That is what we told our investors as they dug deeper into their pockets. Within three months, a mill even more beautiful than the first gold mill, stood shining in the wilds of Manitoba. We were all very proud and tried to assure our nervous investors that the worst was over, and that from here on, success would follow quickly. Technicians were brought in to monitor the first day's production, which once again was on a Friday. Initial results indicated total success, but confirmation would have to await fire assaying of the collected samples. The tired crew was given the weekend to relax before the production startup on Monday. The weather was very dry, and we all congratulated ourselves on our almost miraculous recovery. Monday morning came and we set out for the mill early. But, when we approached the site, we could smell smoke. As we rounded the last corner, we were greeted by the smoldering ruins. The once 80 foot majestic mill was now 12 inches of smoldering ashes. The guard told us that he had been awakened in the middle of the night by spectacular explosions that lit up the sky. The plant was destroyed within minutes. A later RCMP investigation *concluded arson*, probably by one of the nervous investors, all of whom had recouped their money from insurance. Thus, we had been introduced to our first golden rule, Rule # 1, The answer to "What will go wrong?" is just about *"Everything!"*

The year was 1980. A search was carried out to find an appropriate gold property to test the constantly modified differential charge recovery system (DCRS). As was usually the case, a major discovery improving the system was made *accidentally*. Tests were being run in the plant in Calgary. Electric meters had been placed at all strategic points in the system to constantly measure the voltages. Then the lights went out in the city which suffered a massive power failure. Inside the plant meters were showing that electrical currents were still flowing, some points in the system more than others. The currents could not be coming from the positive electrodes through which the slurry flowed, as they had no external electric current. Where then were the electric currents being generated? Back to the books.

$\mathbf{A}$ll we had was water and air flowing in what we later determined was a ground insulated system. Had we somehow tapped the source of lightening? Experts on the electrification of thunderclouds were divided on the actual mechanism, which is still true to this day. What is known is that water droplets in the air become positively charged while the air becomes negatively charged. After a rain, the *"fresh air"* is attributed to the negative electrification of the air which bathes your body's positively charged surface (from negative biochemical activity within), thereby satisfying the charge and producing the *"fresh"* sensation. The positively charged water droplets amass into electric fields containing hundreds of millions of volts. The negative charge from the ground is drawn up towards this massive positive charge until it finally arcs and back-flashes in a lightening bolt. The reason for the charge buildup is in the chemistry (which can be defined as *"microphysics"*) of the participants, water and air. To begin with, air is made up, 99%, of nitrogen and oxygen, which have the distinctive physical property of being two of the three most *"electronegative"* elements known to man, the third is flourine. Electronegativity is defined as the tenacity to extract electrons. Water on the other hand, because of its polarity, readily gives up its electrons. Polarity allows the charge created by the displaced electrons to shuffle and create charged fields within the water. Thus, Mother Nature could not have created a more perfect combination of participants for creating electrical charge

71

differentials. To simply demonstrate the principle, turn on your tap and then put the positive electrode from a volt meter into the stream of water and then put the negative electrode on the grounded metal drain. The voltmeter will register voltage. When our plant in Calgary was suffering from a massive power failure, the volt meters were registering up to 900 millivolts. It was quickly discovered that by changing the configuration of the equipment and increasing the velocity of the insulated slurry (a 40-foot section of plastic pipe with the slurry swirling inside was required), the required increased voltage could be *"induced"* thereby allowing the removal of the submerged positive electrodes, that had been hooked to an external power supply, which dramatically simplified the system. It was also found that the slurry swirl inside the plastic pipe provided an additional benefit, the liberation of much of the gold from its attached ore.

A very coarse placer deposit was located in the Tatamagouche Creek in the Yukon. It became the source for Professor Gordon Briggs' gold scam previously described. The technology indeed proved effective at both dramatically increasing the fine gold recovery, and in simplifying the gold cleanup. Lots of gold! Lots of money! What could go wrong? The answer is once again golden rule # 1, The answer to "What will go wrong?" is *"Everything!"* Bruce, a rather big man who was the project foreman, responded to the roar from a wild animal by twirling instantly around on his feet. His eyes looked directly into the "kneecaps" of a Kodiac Grizzly standing upright waving his upper arms and spewing a foul odor in his breath. It took only a fraction of a second for Bruce to continue swirling around and, faster than a olympic sprinter, race across the site, knocking down fellow workers, with his Kodiac friend a few feet behind. Bruce dived under a big truck to escape the fangs of his new friend, who seemed to want to eat only Bruce. We were in a Kulane National Park, so it was against the law to have firearms, and if you shot any animal it was automatic jail time. Bruce was on his own. The bear eventually tired and left the site. From that moment on it was difficult to get anyone to work. There was more than one Kodiac

Grizzly, four to be exact, each of whom took turns charging down the hills to chase our workers.

Once, I was eating with the men in the camp cookhouse, when we were disturbed by the yapping of a dog running through the camp, closely followed by the naked well-endowed woman cook who quickly flopped through the camp to the security of her bunkhouse. For the next while, we had to cook our own food as the cook would not venture from her bunkhouse. To make matters worse, almost every day government helicopters hovered overhead to monitor the safety of the bears, who killed by swatting off the heads of their prey. Finally, the government trapped the bears and removed them to another distant location. All was well for at least two weeks before we were all once again entertained by our naked cook being chased through the camp. The bears had returned. The net result was that, although the technology worked, the project was a financial bust due to the numerous shutdowns caused by bear attacks. What else could go wrong, other than having the last, and biggest gold clean up stolen by Professor Briggs. Gold mining is definitely not an easy business.

The next opportunity to improve the system came from the Blackhawk mine in Central City Colorado. The ore in this part of the country has undergone more metallurgical examination than any other ore in America. The region has a history of massive production and is home to the famous *Glory Hole*. The ore in this region contains 45% free milling gold and 55% of gold attached to pyrites (iron sulfides). Although the free milling gold can be amalgamated, the sulfide gold must be floated to concentrate it. Since the ore contains 18% pyrite, this means that the maximum improvement by collecting the pyrite is a five-fold concentrate. According to the nearby Colorado School of Mines, floating followed by cyanidation along with gravity recovery of the free milling gold results in about an 80% recovery, but *"only if"* the grade of the ore is at least 0.30 oz/ton. The efficiency of recovery drops dramatically if the grade drops below the 0.30 oz/ton range. Geologists and engineers from the Colorado School of Mines had assured our investors that the grade from our Blackhawk mine would exceed 0.35 oz/ton. What could go wrong? Well, the ore ribboned (thickened to 6 feet and thinned to 8 inches). Mining the required minimum of 5 feet resulted in a mill feed dilution with the average ore at 0.13 oz/ton. However, it was sometime before we realized that the grade was low. We knew that the DCRS system would recover almost all of the 45% of the free milling gold, but the 55% of pyrite gold would require another system.

When the moving insulated slurry is positively charged, the more conductive metals, such as gold or copper readily take on the charge. The free milling metals are therefore readily recovered by the oppositely charged collector. The gold attached to the mineral also receives some charge, but the net charge on the metal-mineral is much less than the metal by itself (differential charging). Therefore, another system would be required. In the plant in Calgary, experimentation with slowing the velocity of the slurry prior to flowing it over a negatively charged rubber belting covered in pear-shaped cups, appeared to be successful recovering the pyrite-containing gold which readily stuck to the charged cups.

The system was called the *"Automat."* An automat was installed in the Blackhawk mill operating at 200 tons per day. The result was the recovery of 4 tons per day of pyrite concentrates. The engineers monitoring the situation expressed concerns when they saw most of the pyrite going into the tailings. However, the tailing assayed only 0.02 oz/ton, and that was from a 0.13 oz/ton head ore, for a *recovery efficiency of 85%*, which was unheard of for an ore of such a low grade. It was also discovered that by running the 4 tons per day of Automat concentrates (as it was produced) through an impact mill with bleach added (sodium hypochlorite), the gold became detached from the pyrite and then by pumping this slurry into the head feed, this gold was recovered by the primary DCRS process. Thus, the research was successful. We had concentrated sulfide ore and extracted the gold with the Automat at a rate of 200 tons per day and extracted all of the liberated gold with the Amtrap, and all at an efficiency of 85% on a low grade ore which, because of the small recovery, left our investors very disenchanted. One subsequently asked, "If the operation was such a success, why did the patient die?" True, but we had demonstrated in a production mode that differential charging of ores could be used to simultaneously recover free gold while concentrating complex gold minerals. In addition, we had successfully used bleach to detach the gold from the sulfides so that the Amtrap could recover it.

The year was 1981, and the project was to develop a totally insulative system. Up to this time the system had been insulated from ground by using wood supports. An operation was set up on the Colorado river near Moab, Utah. The previous operation was shutting down because of obvious (visible) fine gold in the tailings. Initially, although low grade, the efficiencies of recovery were great. Then "gradually the efficiencies worsened." To improve the recovery, as much as 70,000 volts were applied to the negative collector plates. Not only did significant losses still exist, but these latter tests made it obvious, through several mini electrocutions, that feed-back grounding was occurring from the slurry feed systems. The wood ground supports had become water soaked and full of salts which made them increasingly conductive. To rectify this, the system was mounted in a rubber tire-insulated truck and the tests were repeated without the high voltage. This time the efficiencies were once again excellent. From this time on, the system would always be insulated with rubber tires. The men named the truck *"Mongoose #1,"* as a mongoose is a snake killer, and the gold industry is full of two legged snakes.

Our work in Utah was constantly being interrupted by a hoard of government agencies, most of whom did not want our presence on the Colorado River. We expected and were prepared for the environmental and safety agencies, but it seemed that not a week went by without another shutdown. Prior to startup we had visited 8 State and Federal agencies and had been given their clearances. But, new government agencies came out of the woodwork. The 12th agency that threatened to shut us down was the Army Corps of Engineers. Apparently, whoever takes over a placer operation on the Colorado River is responsible to clean up the mess made by previous miners, even if it was done 100 years previously. These people were the good guys. When they saw how our Yukon style triple dike system cleaned up the water from the tailings so that you could actually drink the water being returned to the river, they instructed us to "continue the good work."

Then a few days later, a bearded creature was seen on the other side of the river taking pictures at all angles of our operation. Within an hour he arrived on site to the greeting, "Hello number 13. Who do you represent? Probably the Mormon Mothers of the Miners." He responded, "Close. But actually I represent the Utah Dike Commission and your dikes are over the 18 foot allowable, and without a permit. You are going to have to shut down immediately." "Nonsense," I responded as I ordered the cat operator to "take three feet off the top of the dikes," which were 20 feet high at the time. We were ordered to shut down, as pictorial evidence had proven we had been in conflict with the law. We could, however, take up our case with the Utah Dike Commission, which would be having its next meeting in eight months. In our short history, we had been flooded out, burned out, chased out by bears, swindled out, had lost out due to engineering incompetence, and now we were facing the worst gold miners nightmare. We were being *"kicked out"* by the blind and arrogant government civil service. To the dismay of our investors, we packed up our bags and left.

The year was still 1981, and we were finally being provided with a golden opportunity. A professional, industry-respected geologist had acquired proven and substantial reserves of low grade sulfide dump ore. When brought to the surface, 100 years previously, the miners would hand pick the high grade ore and send it to the mill. The low grade ore, usually sulfides, was "dumped" into a pile. Over a century of rain and weathering, most of the sulfides in the dump ore had oxidized, thereby liberating the gold. A great deal of clay was also generated making conventional

76

recovery difficult. To make things worse, a State fishery was located a few miles downstream. This would be a good test for the environmentally friendly DCRS process. What could go wrong?

Bench scale tests had determined that if the ore were pulverized, 90% recovery could be achieved, and if it were not pulverized, the recovery would be in the 70% range. Since the ore dumps were located in a remote region near Redding, California, it was determined that the extra 20% recovery would not be worth the extra investment capital that would be needed to pulverize the ore. A triple deck vibrating screen was used to process the uncrushed ore at 40 tons per hour (1,000 tons per day). The high clay content did not prove to be a problem, even when it increased substantially as the clay filled water was re-circulated. The 60 feet of 8-inch plastic pipe used to swirl the aerated slurry onto the system proved to be a very efficient method for developing electrostatic induced charge on the slurry of invisible hard rock gold. The recovery was 72% as predicted, and volumes of produced gold was being hauled off to the investors by the happy geologist. The first pile was finished to the investor's chorus of *"where is the gold?"* Apparently both the gold and the geologist had "mysteriously disappeared," and with them, went our project. We could now add *"theft"* to the list of what could go wrong.

The year was 1982, and we were given the opportunity to determine whether the DCRS process would recover natural microscopic mercury coated gold. The location was Ion, Nevada. Conventional systems for the recovery of such gold, such as cyaniding and gravity systems were dramatically inhibited by the mercury coating the gold. A visiting field engineer watched as 83% of the gold and all of the mercury was recovered. His name was Rupert Spivey and he was famous for holding the world record on the most ore moved in one day. He stated that what he had witnessed was *"incredible,"* and therefore no one was going to believe him. His prediction came true, and *"disbelief"* was added to the list of what could go wrong.

The year was 1983, and we were given another chance, after being kicked out of Utah, to determine the capability of the DCRS process on recovering ultra fine alluvial gold. The deposit was located in Gold Gulch, New Mexico, which is historically famous for its fine placer gold that is difficult if not impossible to recover economically. Over 2,000 cubic yards were processed with an average efficiency of 90% compared to 25% using conventional systems. Despite this high efficiency of recovery, the ore was too marginal to sustain production.

The same year, another opportunity arose to determine whether oxide or organic coatings on the surface of the gold would, because of their insulative properties, inhibit the differential charge effects. The location was La Salle Mountain, Utah. Although the gold contents were not high, the extremely high efficiencies of recovery proved that the oxide and organic coatings did not inhibit the differential recovery of the gold.

Also the same year, bench scale tests were carried out to see if differential charging could concentrate both tin ore and lead/silver ore. Twenty-one thousand grams of cassiterite (tin ore) at 0.12% tin (or a total of 25.2 grams of tin), were processed producing 110 grams of concentrate at 21.6% tin (or 23.8 grams of tin) with 1.5 grams of tin in the tailings, indicating 94% recovery of the tin. The DCRS process appears to work on tin ore. Also, 794 pounds of waste rock (0.5 inch) at 7 oz/ton silver and 8.7 % lead were processed without pulverizing and produced 108 pounds at 43 % silver and 21.4% lead for a total recovery of 33 % of the silver. The DCRS process produced an inexpensive refinery acceptable concentrate without pulverizing, even though the efficiency was low, which did not matter as the waste rock dumps were massive.

In 1983, we were also given the chance to determine whether differential charging could be used to recover metallic platinum in placer ores. Most alluvial gold deposits contain some minor portion of platinum metal, most of which is not recovered as it is most always much finer than the gold. The ore sample was taken from the Tulameen River in British Columbia., and was processed through a bench scale unit. One hundred pounds were processed producing 10 pounds of concentrates which were then electro-amalgamated with sodium metal added to the mercury so that the platinum would report to the amalgam. Sixty-seven milligrams of gold (0.043 oz/ton) were recovered along with 47 milligrams of blacks containing visible platinum and assaying 7 milligrams of platinum. Historically, the ratio of gold to platinum from the Tulameen is 10 to one, which was identical to the DCRS recovery. Thus differential charging appears to work, as predicted, with high platinum metal recoveries.

At last, in 1983, DCRS was given an opportunity to test its equipment in a production mode. The overriding question was durability or wear factor of the equipment. The opportunity was an operational placer in Eureka Creek, Yukon. The placer was operating at 10,000 tons per day, while the DCRS equipment operated at a maximum of 1,000 tons per day. Therefore, the placer tailings shute was divided into 10 portions, each of which should be tested. The results were two-fold. First, the recovery of running one-tenth of the tailings (1,000 tons per day) on many days yielded more gold than the placer operator processing the original 10,000 tons per day. Secondly, the highest recoveries came from the center shute.

At the termination of the testing, after 4 months, the assessment was that the placer operator recovered **18%** of the gold (as was predicted in the engineering books) with DCRS recovering 7.2 % (from one-tenth of the tailings or a projected **72%** if the total tailings had been run). The second result was the wear factors, which were severe after 50,000 tons, necessitating further testing of materials. The placer operator was ecstatic, and wanted 10 units built and installed immediately. His request was reluctantly refused as patent law is specific that commercial production would be deemed as *public disclosure* which would cause any patent application to be disallowed. Thus, we could get into immediate gold production, but lose our patent. The investment to this date was substantially more than the gold produced. This brought reality to the golden rule, *#2 Even when you win, you lose.*

By 1984, new and more durable materials, Swedish rubber, high density plastic and ore deflectors, were being employed into the DCRS equipment, all requiring durability testing. The opportunity came from the Bar-F Placer Mine nears Wells, British Columbia. The normal placer recovery of gold was 25% with 3% of this gold being smaller than 8 mesh (the measure for jewelry gold is bigger than 8 mesh). The new DCRS system was assessed at 90% recovery with 78% of this recovery less than 8 mesh. There were also no physical indications of wear on most of the equipment. The project was another *technical success.*

Industrial research proved to be very costly, forcing the creation of ingenious investment schemes. Fortunately, the Canadian government came up with a scheme called the *Scientific Research Tax Credit or SRTC.* A research company could offer a tax credit to an individual or corporation, for which they would receive a 50% tax credit, which was instantly cashed by the government. For example, we could offer a corporation a million dollar tax credit, immediately return a half-million dollars and the corporation could get another half million dollar tax credit from the government. Thus, we ended up with a half-million dollars and the corporation got all of its money back immediately and retained an interest in the project. Sounds fantastic! What could go wrong?

Well, in 2 years, SCTCs set research in Canada back 10 years as many researchers were forced to leave the country. Many of the same politicians who *"accidentally forgot"* to cap commissions on the transactions, initially participated with 3% commissions which quickly rose to 50%. Instant fortunes were made as ingenious scam research projects were developed to "take advantage of the commissions." In the waning hours of the program, from a $10 million SRTC, our corporate sponsor received its $5 million back and a $5 million tax credit. The middle men got $3 million. We were left with just $2 million.

With dozens of these transactions occurring in rapid succession, most based on illegitimate research projects, public outcrys quickly terminated the SRTC program. Even though we had previously been taxed for 10 years as a research group with a laboratory, technicians and PhDs doing legitimate research, our SRTC was cancelled on the basis that *"no research was being done."* Since the Canadian government refused to believe that research on gold was being done, we immediately placed the Differential Charge Recovery System offshore in Barbados. All of our assets, lab equipment, computers and files were soon seized. We were guilty until we could prove ourselves innocent, and before we could take the government to court, we had to be tried first in the government *kangaroo tax court*, after which we could appeal in federal court. With the belief that the truth would allow us to win our case and have our assets restored, a few nervous investors, due to the enormous upside, decided to take a chance on us.

The following four years saw constant legal work as we had been convicted on schedule by the kangaroo court. We continued with numerous lab and field tests to perfect the technology, until finally in 1988, after 10 years of research, a patent was applied for. The next day, professional geologist, Guy Salizar, led a public demonstration of the technology where 100 invited guests from the mining industry were given vials of gold and told to add them, or not add them, to each pile of virgin placer ore which each group was assigned, and then each group process its own pile of ore to recover their own gold. All of the recoveries were in the 90% plus range. Offers began flooding in.

Finally, in January 1991 we had earned the right, by paying for it, to take the federal government to court. Many other legitimate researchers could not afford the legal work required to get justice, and had already left to carry their research on in other countries. We knew our case was strong as we had retained industry recognized giants to testify on our behalf. It would take time and money, but we knew we would win. Then, one hour before trial, the government lawyers conceded the validity of our case and offered a *"consent judgement."* The only thing that remained was to calculate how much the government owed to us. I personally wanted to fight in court, as the years of dealing with civil servants had taught me that they could not be trusted. Our lawyers argued that pursuing the case in court would be fruitless and a waste of money, as we could not win any more than what they had already conceded. Well, our prestigious high paid law firm was wrong. If we had won in court, the government would have been ordered by the judge to pay immediately what they owe us. But, by conceding out of court, the government has *"reasonable time"* to pay. The private individual is given 10 days, but the government is given "reasonable time." But who defines "reasonable"? The government, of course, who have found a million and one reasons to delay as they pass the case from civil servant to civil servant. In the more than 7 years that have elapsed, the law firm has been *shamelessly silent*, and the government has been ignorant, but always cooperative. The truth is that the law firm would jeopardize other cases by pursuing this one, which has *embarrassed* the government; thus, they have no intention of rocking the boat by doing their duty. As for the government, they know the squeeze play they have on the law firm will allow them to defy the courts and never pay what they legally owe, approximately $3 million. They hope that we will get tired and just go away. Even the current Canadian Prime Minister shamelessly made money from SRTCs. The bottom line is that when the government is behind you, it is dangerous to bend over. We took our chances and *whaaaammm!!!* Our law firm, on the other hand, should be ashamed of itself. Their action, or lack of action, is the reason why lawyers are made the butt of so many jokes. Such as, three doctors scrubbing after surgery. First doctor: "I had the easiest surgery, as I operated on an accountant and when I opened her up, everything was numbered, ..1..2..3." Second doctor: "No my surgery was easier, as I operated on an engineer and when you're finished and have a few parts left over, they never seem to mind." Third, older and experienced doctor: "You are both wrong! It is easiest to operate on a lawyer as they are heartless, spineless and gutless and you can exchange their heads for their rear ends."

CHAPTER THIRTEEN

THE FAILURE TO EXPLOIT THE DIFFERENTIAL CHARGE RECOVERY SYSTEM, (DCRS)

From the instant the patent was applied for, it was agreed that the best way of getting the technology out and into the mining industry would be with a world-class operating mine. Sounds easy until you remember that 99% of gold prospects fail and that those already producing gold apply the golden rule *#3 The man who has the gold makes the rules*, which means that under no circumstance will they do anything to jeopardize their gold production, especially by trying new processes. Remember, the froth floatation patent now used by almost all gold mining companies was not even tried by them for 40 years. Such is the history of mining.

The first opportunity came from the jungle in the Osa Peninsula in Costa Rica. One of the participants at the public disclosure demonstration had been so impressed, that he agreed to have the equipment installed on his prolific operation high on the Rincon River. A visit to the site shows the local oreros (gold miners) recovering substantial gold by hand panning. Tests showed that they were losing substantial fine gold. They were eager to see the DCRS process on their river. We applied for, and received all of the necessary government permits. Excitedly, we constructed and shipped the *Mongoose #2* to Costa Rica. Once in Costa Rica, what could go wrong?

First of all, the country is run on a system of bribes. To get anything done, you have to pay bribes known as *"tips."* Large numbers of children are employed as *"runners,"* whose only job is to run the bribes from one person to the other. A suitcase full of colones (we referred to this money as phony colones) was required to get the equipment out of customs. Then a truck, with an engine the size of a tiny Volkswagon engine (the only truck available), was hired to slowly, slowly haul the 40 foot unit out to the Osa Peninsula on the Trans America Highway, which has more pot holes than tar. Although only a few hundred miles, the truck took one week to arrive at the mouth of the Rincon River, from where a cat was used to transport it upriver. Prior to reaching the site, we were informed by our Costa Rican partner that we would initially be testing two miles downstream from the rich claims which were in production. We were informed that the new claims had been tested and found to be *"just as rich,"* and that campsite had been built on site. What could go wrong?

We arrived on the site, hot and exhausted. After a delicious meal, I was shown to the shower stalls. I should have known that something was wrong, as so many eyes were watching "the boss." I was just finishing, looking up to rinse off, when a hand-size, poisonous spider dropped onto my shoulder. The air was filled with laughter as I raced through the camp, flipping naked, back and forth, trying to swat off the beast. Finally successful, I stood naked and silently watched as the spider slowly crawled off into the jungle.

That night, I was so tired that I slept though a noisy television gunfight. In the morning I woke up to streams of light passing through holes in the grass thatched hut. To begin with, there was no electricity in the camp and therefore no television. The far side of the Rincon River is a rainforest, protected by the United Nations who pay government troops to shoot any oreros panning the rich rainforest placers. The night I arrived, the troops arrived and a fight ensued. Everyone in camp fled to the safety of the jungle, except for me, I had slept through it all.

That same morning an orero came into camp seeking medical help. He had been bitten by a wild pig in the jungle. He had a fist size hunk of muscle missing from his calf. The wild pigs in the jungle do this hoping their victims drop to their knees so that they can attack them more ferociously. This orero survived, but was in trouble. I packed his wound with all of my travel supply of antibiotics and drove him down to the mouth of the Rincon where I phoned for a plane to evacuate him to a hospital, which is free in Costa Rica. Upon his return one week later, he thanked me by taking me to the forbidden zone, the rainforest. He showed me a three quart glass jar, full to the brim with nuggets, and the uttered the word *"Eldorado."* I had read in the local books that the Indians had taken a Spanish missionary blindfolded to see Eldorado. He described crossing the river 7 times as they traveled up river. That was the same number of times that I had to cross the Rincon to reach the site. The missionary then described the scene as they took off his blindfold. The jungle trees were so thick and tall that he could only see a sliver of blue sky. That was exactly what I was looking at. Also, Spanish records claimed that Eldorado was protected by fierce Indians using poison blow darts. That description perfectly described the Osa Indians. Finally, many South American cultures record in their history the purchase of gold from the Indians on the *"west"* coast of Costa Rica. The only gold production on the west coast came from the Osa Peninsula. Today, a few Indians work the rich placers of Eldorado by hand, while cautiously watching for government troops.

After spending two months on the snake infested river (poisonous snakes had killed 17 oreros in just the past 6 months) setting up the DCRS equipment, it soon became obvious that the ore was very lean in gold. Upon investigating the test done the previous year, it was learned that the ore samples were run in a sluice box which had been **contaminated** previously when it had been used to clean up concentrates. We immediately requested permission to move on up river to the richer location, only to find out that the claims were **in litigation** as our Costa Rican partner had been caught by the government smuggling the produced gold to try to eliminate paying royalties. **"Partners that lie"** had now been added to reasons for failing in gold mining.

Upon returning from Costa Rica, a location was sought to develop the DCRS technology for commercial use. An old gold mill near Wickenburg, Arizona was chosen, as within a 60 mile radius of the mill there had been 160 gold mines. Also the mill was an all-year operation with ample water. Ores from dozens of old mines were tested. Then, in 1988, a mine was purchased so that the final design for commercial production could be perfected. The mine was the **Mystic Mine** and it contained a million dollars worth of "proven reserves" that could be recovered with the DCRS system for under one-half million dollars. What could go wrong?

At first, nothing. The ore was delivered by truck and the efficiency of recovery was established at 84%. Bullion refinery receipts were rich and plentiful, but the tailings were too high. It was decided to use two systems in series to improve recovery, and it worked. Recovery rose to 92%. The final design would be one unit stacked on top of the other. Then the ore grade began to drop dramatically. Unconsolidated wall rock was falling into the ore causing **"dilution."** Then, an **"unexpected monsoon"** caused flooding which blocked off the roads. This was aggravated by the regional dam **"opening up its overflow"** (causing the roads to be submerged) to prevent the dam from bursting. What else could go wrong? More monsoons, more floods? In the end, the amount of gold in the proven reserves was indeed recovered; however, twice as much ore had to be processed and it took twice as long, making the project a break-even endeavor. Mining had proven to be very difficult. Thus, much of the next few years was spent "evaluating" a **"massive new gold resource,"** unassayable invisible gold.

CHAPTER FOURTEEN

THE RECOVERY OF UNASSAYABLE INVISIBLE GOLD

I am often asked, "what is the best gold mine that you ever saw ?" Well I have seen some deliriously rich deposits, and I know I will see many more. But, the biggest and most massive deposit of gold can be found lying right beneath our noses, *trillions of ounces*. Invisible because it is difficult to assay and because of our ignorance. The gold occurs as sulfate salt-encapsulated micron gold. In nature it is found in hematite (hydrated iron oxide) sand, massive deposits that were produced by melting glaciers and that cover large parts of several states. Salt encapsulated gold can also be found in the sulfide tailings of copper and gold ores. It has remained hidden from man's fire assay gold analyses, as the acid salt reacts with the sodium carbonate in the fire assay flux to generate large volumes of carbon dioxide gas. This propels the encapsulated gold as a froth to the top of the assay cup, where it cannot be entrapped by the scouring lead in the flux (known as *"acid slag effect"* in assay and mining journals such as Peele's Mining Engineering Journal). This assay accuracy problem has been documented and understood since the 1850s. The salt encapsulation also blocks the gold from vision, as well as causing numerous analytical difficulties. However, once the salt has been removed by dissolving it with various water washing procedures, the gold is both assayable by certified fire assay, and is recoverable by techniques that recover micron gold. The acid salts also tend to generate gels and clays that interfere with cyanidation. However, the gold is readily recovered with differential charging.

For decades hundreds of amateur *"clandestine laboratories"* all over the glacial drainage basin covering parts of the four states of Utah, California, Nevada and Arizona (known as *The Great Basin*) have been analyzing such hematite ore using homemade analytical procedures. The results were assays of gold that were well beyond the realm of credibility. The professional critics could not verify the work using the tried and proven certified fire assays, and thus dismissed all such claims as fraudulent. The author, apologetically, admits to being part of the ignorant professional chorus. Actually, the procedures used by most of the clandestine labs were derivatives of the totally acceptable procedure of *"re-firing"* the cup and cupel for two or more times. Furthermore, the assay problems caused by acid slag are well documented in both assay and mining journals. The reason that the professional community was unable to reproduce the high results was that neither they nor their amateur counterparts recognized the problem, and, therefore, did not understand that the samples changed dramatically over time due to dehydration, which increases salt precipitation and encapsulation. Recently, the problem of time, in assaying these ores, has been recognized, and the term *"time sensitive ore"* has been coined.

Professional geologists reject the clandestine lab findings for the following reasons:
1. They are unable to verify the results with third-party certified fire assays.
2. They are unable to duplicate the results with the same procedure in third-party labs.
3. They are unable to see the gold with an electron microscope.
4. The grade of the gold in each deposit is always too high to be explained by any known geological circumstance.

5. The thickness and extent of each deposit is so vast that the reserves implied by each deposit would surpass the current world gold reserves already mined.

6. Other professionals, analysts, and metallurgists agree with their conclusions.

7. No one has ever successfully mined such deposits.

With such apparently overwhelming disproving factors, how can anyone continue to justify the existence of such massive gold deposits? Well, as the general public has become accustomed to learning, *"experts"* are usually wrong as many times as they are right. Experts of the day once swore that the world was flat, that man would never fly, and that you would have to be a lunatic to believe that man would ever walk on the moon. Albert Einstein's theory on relativity was so challenged by the experts of the day that they got together and published a rebuking article entitled, *"One Hundred Against Einstein."* Einstein retorted that "if they were right, one would have been enough."

As technology evolves, new answers to old problems are constantly being found. The result is a dramatic shift in the opinion of the expert. Well, even though there had not been any major change in gold technology for more than 100 years, technology had evolved recently in the process of gold extraction from ores. A process of electrically charging metal in a fast moving water slurry and then capturing the metal as it passes over an oppositely charged collector, had been developed. Absolutely no chemicals are used in the process, which can produce concentrates up to thousands of ounces per ton. The patented process is known as the *Differential Charge Recovery System (DCRS)*. Hematite ores that are run from the Great Basin using the DCRS process yield *recoveries* that are dramatically higher than the amount indicated by the certified fire assay of the head ore. Also, the tailings produced by removing the gold using the DCRS process fire assay substantially higher than the head ore. This, of course, appears to be impossible. However, when examining all of the factors, the conclusion has to be the unthinkable, that the fire assays are incorrect. Once it is recognized that the fire assays suffer from the acid slag effect, procedures can be developed to remove the cause, *acid salts*, so that the assays can more accurately reflect the gold content of the hematite ore. This is exactly what happens. Certified fire assays of the washed samples assay many magnitudes higher than certified assays of the unwashed ore. Hence, the partially water washed tailings produced by the DCRS process should indeed assay higher than the unwashed head ore.

Thus, with the washed ore assays now verifying both the existence of gold and the magnitude of the deposits, a viable geological explanation for such a massive deposit that contains *thousands of times the world's gold reserves*, the **Great Basin Gold Discovery**, must be postulated. Conventional geologists have no explanations that could explain such a deposit.

The professional geologists, chemists and metallurgists were wrong to conclude that the gold did not exist in these deposits, and the clandestine chemists were right. Wow !!! Some professional geologists, who have no answers, scoff at the chemist who is attempting to provide a viable explanation by explaining that he believes that the deposits are the direct result of glacial activity. One bemused geologist from the Arizona Department of Mineral Resources, responded that "Chemists should stick to chemistry." Another explained that Arizona has always been too warm for glaciers. However, geology books explain how plate tectonics result in the continents moving apart and drifting over the poles, resulting in maps showing the North Pole existing at a location we now call Tucson, Arizona. To the layman, this means that Arizona, being at the North Pole, was once under ice, and that once again the smug *"experts,"* who steadfastly deny the existence of ice in Arizona, have to be wrong. However, this ice age is not the one that is believed to have created the massive hematite gold deposits. The geological Pleistocene era which created the Great Basin and which ended 30,000 years ago and covered almost all of Europe and half of North America, is believed to be responsible for the numerous and massive gold deposits.

The first question that must be answered is where did all of the gold come from ? The geologist only has explanations that can explain deposits only a tiny fraction of the size of the hematite deposits. Thus, unpublished explanations must be postulated. To begin with, we know that gold comes from the molten bowels of the Earth. Most of the massive gold deposits known today exist thousands of feet below the surface in Pre-Cambrian Rock (over 500 million years old). The real question to be answered is how did such a massive amount of such gold-enriched Pre-Cambrian rock end up on the surface as hematite sand ? When we look at the most massive surface deposit of gold that is known to exist today, we are looking at the Carlin trend which was produced by a massive fault, which lifted the lower Pre-Cambrian ore to the surface, and then flipped over (on its belly) exposing all of the ore at the surface. One golden rule of Nature is that what was proven to have happened once geologically, must also have happened many times before. Then where are the other Carlins ?

Let's suppose, just for the sake of argument, that dozens of Carlins existed in the northern United States and Canada in pre-glacial times. When the glaciers came, they would have ground up these Carlin-type deposits. The amount of ice was so massive that it lowered the surface of the oceans about 650 feet. When this massive amount of ice melted, it released oceans of water and ground-up rock, which was trapped by the mountain ranges in the western United States. This forced the turbulent flow of water and gold bearing Pre-Cambrian rock debris to pass into the Great Basin creating huge glacial lakes. The flowing water flushed the lighter minerals south into Mexico and the Pacific ocean.

The next question to be answered is how did a granitic Pre-Cambric rock end up as a hematite sand? The answer lies in the science of mineral diagenesis, which is a fancy name for the study of how minerals are altered when exposed to the changing environments of nature. If a gold-rich granitic rock is ground up in the laboratory and flushed with large volumes of water for several years, the result would be a hematite residue containing gold. The octahedral micron gold would have been liberated from the sulfides as they oxidized, under water, into sulfates and the resulting sulfuric acid would have reacted with the carbonates to liberate the calcium. The result would be a positively surface charged octahedral gold crystal being surrounded by the negatively charged sulfate ion which subsequently attracts the positively charged calcium ion, resulting in the encapsulation by precipitation of calcium sulfate around the gold. In nature, the oceans of turbulent water move the micron gold as if it were an ion, thus resulting in a relatively even widespread deposit. The breaking ice jams result in the liberation of water tidal waves that flush the clays, generated by the hydration of the granitic feldspars, as well as the soluble salts, south through Mexico and into the Pacific ocean. In summary, the mineral alteration procedure produced by nature can be duplicated in the laboratory, and thus, ***the proposed postulation is viable.***

TABLE #1

Multi-Laboratory Comparison of Certified Assays of Virgin Sample and the Same Samples Treated to Wash Off the Sulfate Salts.

Sample Description	Iron king Labs (Humbolt, AZ)		Mountain states Labs (Tuscon, AZ)		Loring Laboratories (Calgary, Canada)	
	Virgin	Treated**	Virgin	Treated**	Virgin	Treated**
WC-6-Run	0.001	0.180	0.002	0.201	0.006	0.063
78053-Lam	0.006	0.027	0.003	0.035	0.004	0.029
78043-Lam	0.004	0.072	0.005	0.078	0.005	0.063
BRX-36-1	0.006	0.077	0.006	0.043	0.010	0.048
BRX-36-2	0.003	1.096*	0.001	0.051	0.001	0.062
BRX-18-13	0.018	0.055	0.031	0.045	0.032	0.065
IPC-9-1	0.001	0.046	0.003	0.046	0.005	0.041
IPC-010	0.002	0.030	0.001	0.039	0.001	0.074
IPC-9-3	0.003	0.290	0.001	0.331	0.001	0.165
Averages	0.004	0.078	0.008	0.087	0.010	0.061
% Difference		+1950%		+1088%		+610%

Note: All assays were certified.

anomaly, caused by the release of a cluster of gold crystals, was not included in the averaging.
** the samples were treated as follows (note: samples were run in duplicate):
1. 60 grams were weighed into 500 milliliter flasks
2. 100 milliliters of distilled water was added
3. 10 milliliters of sulfuric acid was added and the sample reacted for 15 minutes
4. the flask was brought to volume (500 ml) with distilled water
5. the solution was then subjected to high frequency fibration for 30 minutes
6. the mixture was then filtered using lots of water to wash the residue
7. the residue was then dried in the sun
8. each duplicate sample were blended together, pulverized and split for assay.

TABLE #2

Time Sensitive Ores (Walter Lashley, California Mining Journal 12/92)

Certain ores assayed immediately upon sampling will assay many times higher than when they are assayed several days later. This phenomenon is well known by many researchers, but because no viable explanation could be given, no assays were ever published prior to Lashley's.

Sample #	Fire Assays (oz/ton)	
	New Ore	Old Ore
1	0.44	0.00
2	0.24	0.00
3	0.24	0.00
4	0.23	0.02
5	0.41	0.01
6	0.41	0.01
7	0.42	0.01
8	0.05	0.01
9	0.70	0.00
10	0.34	0.05
11	0.24	0.01
12	0.63	0.04
13	0.15	0.04
A	0.11	0.001
B	0.22	0.001
Average	**0.32**	**0.02**

The phenomenon is due to acid salt precipitation encapsulating the gold as the samples dry slowly over time *(Barefoot Theory)*. The phenomenon is due to water sensitivity, with time only being a factor which determines the degree of dehydration which would result in the precipitation of acid salts to encapsulate the gold.

TABLE #3

Comparison of DCRS Recoveries With the Assays of Both Virgin Hematite Sand Samples and the Same Samples With Their Acid Salts Washed Out.

| Sample | Dry Wt | Soak | DCRS | Recovery | Head Assay (oz/ton) | |
#	(lbs)	time (hr)	mgs	oz/ton	Dry	Washed
Nevada #1	50	12	8.7	0.017	0.001	0.049
Nevada #2	128	12	6.2	0.0031	0.001	0.022
Nevada #3	52	13	5.3	0.0033	0.001	0.008
Nevada #4	47	0	20.0	0.026	0.003	0.030
Nevada #5	47	0	5.0	0.007	0.001	0.007
Nevada #6	47	0	6.0	0.008	0.003	0.002
Nevada #7	47	0	6.0	0.007	0.001	0.003
Nevada #8	47	0	481.0	0.461	0.002	0.118
Nevada #9	47	3	147.0	0.181	0.006	0.219
Nevada #10	47	5	63.0	0.078	0.002	0.004
Nevada #11	47	5	23.0	0.029	0.001	0.010
Nevada #12	47	6	2857.0 *	3.205 *	0.004	0.007
Nevada #13	47	8	287.0	0.353	0.003	0.009
Nevada #14	47	8	291.0	0.358	0.003	0.011
Nevada #15	47	10	57.0	0.071	0.003	0.002
Nevada #16	45	10	40.0	0.051	0.003	lost
Nevada #17	47	11	20.0	0.025	0.002	0.015
Nevada #18	47	12	30.0	0.037	0.002	0.002
Nevada #19	47	22	37.0	0.045	0.004	0.022
Nevada #20	47	25	47.0	0.058	0.004	0.013
Nevada #21	47	26	20.0	0.025	0.002	0.018
Nevada #22	47	45	32.0	0.039	0.002	0.003
Nevada #23	47	48	11.0	0.014	0.003	0.014
Nevada #24	47	49	9.0	0.009	0.001	0.006
Nevada #25	47	50	7.0	0.009	0.003	0.006
Nevada #26	47	3	12.3	0.015	0.037	0.140
Nevada #27	47	7	0.6	0.0007	0.001	0.015
Nevada #28	47	6	5.1	0.0063	0.001	0.003

Nevada #29	47	8	1.9	0.0023	0.001	0.008
Nevada #30	39	9	0.1	0.0002	0.002	0.014
Nevada #31	36	10	0.1	0.0002	0.005	0.009
Nevada #32	47	9	3.4	0.0042	0.001	0.006
Nevada #33	47	9	1.0	0.0012	0.001	0.025
Nevada #34	47	10	23.2	0.0286	0.001	0.009
Nevada #35	44	10	2. 0	0.0026	0.001	0.001
Nevada #36	47	11	0.1	0.0001	0.002	0.036
Nevada #37	47	11	0.1	0.0001	0 .001	0.026
Averages	**49**	**16**	**46.2**	**0.061**	**0.003**	**0.025**

* delete anomaly from averages

TABLE #4

Gold Recoveries Using Various Pre-Soaking or Drying Treatments Prior To Processing Bulk Samples of Water Sensitive Ores and Tailings.

Sample	Weight tons	Treatment	Certified Assay oz/ton	Recovery oz/ton	$/ton	Tails oz/ton
Nevada Hematite #1	6.0	1 day drying	0.001	0.011	4.12	0.018
California Hematite#1	22.6	rain soaked	0.004	0.019	7.30	0.016
Nevada Hematite #2	16.0	rain soaked	0.011	0.022	8.32	0.047
Arizona Hematite# 4	23.3	7 day drying	0.003	0.001	0.45	0.004
Arizona Hematite# 4	19.5	20 hour soak	0.003	0.014	5.20	0.004
Colorado Tails #1	11.2	60 hour soak	0.236	0.336	127.70	0.022
Colorado Tails #2	11.7	60 hour soak	0.027	0.016	6.08	0.025
AZ Copper Tails #1	14.9	60 hours soak	0.002	0.0044	1.67	0.070
AZ Copper Tails #2	17.5	24 hour soak	0.002	0.0031	1.18	0.001
AZ Hematite Ore	14.0	24 hour soak	0.003	0.0126	7.20	0.009
AZ Hematite Sand	21.0	60 hour soak	0.003	0.0095	3.60	0.001
Average (5)	18.6	soaked hematite	0.005	0.015	6.32	0.015
Average (2)	14.7	dried hematite	0.002	0.006	2.28	0.011
Average (2)	11.5	gold tailings	0.118	0.176	66.89	0.024
Average (2)	17.5	copper tailings	0.003	0.011	5.40	0.005

Note: Gold calculated at $400/ton.

Comments:

1. Even the bulk sample that had not been soaked, Nevada #1, yielded more gold (0.011 oz/t) than the certified fire assay of the head sample   (0.001 oz./t).
2. The rain-soaked samples yielded much higher recoveries than the certified fire assays of their head samples and their corres-

ponding tailings samples, after recovering the gold, were four times as high as the head samples. The slurry tailings samples were allowed to settle for several days before siphoning off the water thereby removing most of the acid salts that inhibit the fire assaying procedure.

3. The 20 hour soaked Maxam #4 bulk sample yielded 14 times as much gold as the same sample that was dried for 7 days, once again demonstrating the effects of dehydration on the precipitation of gold encapsulating acid salts.

4. The recovery of gold plus the gold remaining in the tailings from the processing of the sulfide tailings (Leadville Tails) and the copper tailings (Cypress) was substantially higher than the gold analyzed in the head samples. The oxidation of the sulfides produces sulfates that precipitate as acid salts encapsulating much of the gold.

5. Pre-soaking the ore, in most cases, generated higher recoveries of gold than the fire assays of the head ore.

GLACIATION

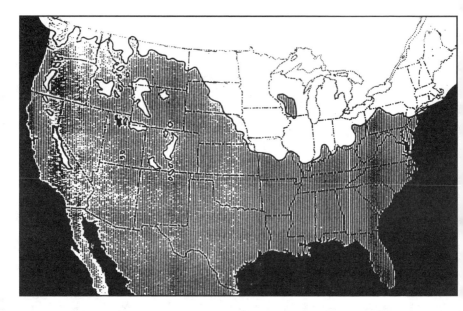

The limits of Pleistocene glaciation (white) in North America.

LAKES PRODUCED IN THE GREAT BASIN
AS THE RESULT OF GLACIERS MELTING

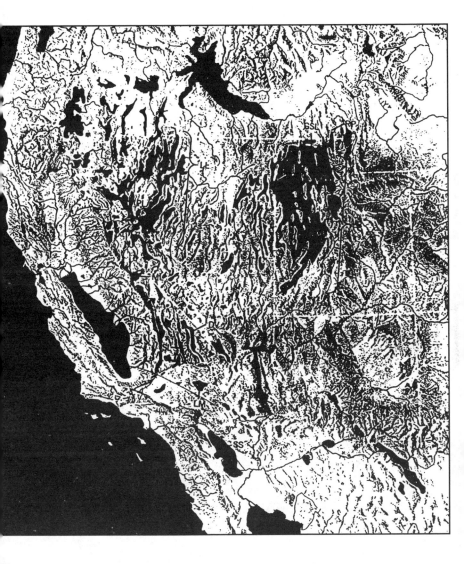

Table #1 demonstrates how, just by washing out the salt encapsulating the gold, certified assayers found up to 20 times as much gold in the same sample. Table #2 shows how the samples are *"time sensitive"* and how the assay result is 16 times as much gold by assaying immediately rather than later after the salts have had time to dry and harden. Table #3 shows how the DCRS process was able to recover 20 times as much gold as the certified assays on numerous samples representing massive Nevada deposits. It also showed how water washing the samples resulted in increasing assays by 8 times. Table #4 shows how samples from Arizona, Nevada, California and Colorado, processed *by the truckload* resulted in recoveries by the DCRS process that were, on average, *"3 times as high as the certified assays"* Table #4 also shows more gold in the water washed tailings assays, after DCRS recovered the gold, than in the head assays. All of these tables represent only some of the work done. The remainder of the work only reinforces the numbers provided in these four tables.

In one particular bulk-run experiment, three truckloads of the same blended ore from an Arizona glacial deposit were processed in three separate tests. In one test, the truckload of ore was submerged in water and processed the next day resulting in $5.20/ton worth of gold. In the second test, the truck was also submerged in water, but the ore was put into a tank for a week and circulated before processing resulting in $8.20/ton worth of gold being recovered. The third test saw the ore dried in the desert sun for one week before being processed resulting in a recovery of $0.45/ton worth of gold.

The preliminary work has been done. The ore deposit has been discovered. Analytical procedures employing a pre-wash procedure prior to certified assaying has been developed. Some partial success has been attained in processing the ore by the truckload using the DCRS process. Work must now focus on the bulk treatment of the ore to remove the salts prior to processing. *The world's largest gold mine awaits!*

CHAPTER FIFTEEN

PORPHYRY COPPER GOLD

Also when I am often asked "What is the best gold mine that you ever saw?" I not only think of the Great Basin gold deposit that lies beyond the assayer's eyes, but I also think of the porphyry copper gold that also lies beyond the assayer's eyes. Invisible because it is difficult to assay and also because of our ignorance. The gold occurs as sulfate salt-encapsulated micron gold. In nature it is found in hematite (hydrated iron oxide) sand, massive deposits that were produced by melting glaciers and that cover large parts of several states. Salt encapsulated gold can also be found in the sulfate tailings of copper and gold ores causing the assays of gold to be incorrectly low.

Most massive porphry copper deposits found near the Continental Divide, were initially discovered as low grade surface gold deposits with grades approximately 0.10 oz/ton. Deeper mining led to more copper, but less gold. The gold was difficult to process and as the grades dropped, so the mines switched to processing the copper, an average of 10 pounds per ton. As copper is a low-priced metal, often 70 cents per pound, the $7.00 per ton grade necessitated massive production to lower the costs per ton of processing. A $1.00-per-ton profit is considered good, especially since these mines often operate at a loss. Thus, recovery of even a small amount of gold could be significant. Most porphyry copper mines produce significant gold (Table #1), averaging $2.62 per ton, with the Arizona mines, Morenci, Chino and Tyrone being the lowest (recoveries averaging $0.16 per ton).

TABLE #1
Gold Production of Various Porphyry Copper Deposits

Deposit & Location	Annual Ore MM Tons	Gold Recovered 1000s oz	oz/ton	$/ton
Kennecott 1965	57	405	0.0072	2.16
Kennecott 1970	70	404	0.0059	1.77
Kennecott 1972	59	350	0.0060	1.80
Bigham 1992	1240	8060	0.0065	1.95
New Cornella, AZ	255	138	0.0054	1.62
Battle Mtn Canyon	39	975	0.0025	7.50
Battle Mtn Basin	26	286	0.0011	3.30
Satuluv			0.0015	4.50
Bouganville	32	500	0.0156	4.68
Ertsberg	3	68	0.0272	8.16
Biga	12	20	0.0017	0.50
Toledo	13	23	0.0018	0.54.
Labo	7	51	0.0076	2.28
Santo Thomas	7	75	0.0112	3.36
Morenci	43	16	0.0004	0.12
Tyrone	16	6	0.0004	0.12
Chino	17	17	0.0010	0.30
Average	119	712	0.0087	2.62

Although the recoveries of the Arizona mines were low, and the fire assays apparently confirming reasonable recoveries, acid slag effect was highly probable, and tests proved there was at least 10 times as much gold as was originally assayed (see Table #6).

TABLE #2

Comparison of assays by three certified laboratories on the same samples that had been submitted both with and without a treatment of washing the acid salts out of the sample. The samples were porphyry copper samples from Arizona mines provided by the Chief Chemist of Phelps Dodge.

	Chemex Laboratories (Reno Nevada)		Iron King Laboratories (Humbolt Arizona)		Loring Laboratories (Calgary Canada)	
Before Treatment: (virgin samples)						
	Fire Assay		Fire Assay		Fire Assay	
	oz/ton	$/ton	oz/ton	$/ton	oz/ton	$/ton
	0.002	0.70	0.018	6.30	0.002	0.70
	0.007	2.45	0.012	4.20	0.001	0.35
	0.002	0.70	0.008	2.80	0.001	0.35
	0.003	1.05	0.010	3.50	0.002	0.70
Average	0.004	1.24	0.012	4.20	0.002	0.53
After Treatment: (washed samples.)						
	Fire Assay		Fire Assay		Fire Assay	
	oz/ton	$/ton	oz/ton	$/ton	oz/ton	$/ton
	0.014	4.90	0.026	9.10	0.012	4.20
	0.014	4.90	0.022	7.70	0.012	4.20
	0.018	4.30	0.018	6.30	0.011	3.85
	0.014	4.90	0.016	5.60	0.019	6.65
Average	0.015	5.25	0.021	7.18	0.014	4.73

Note: 1. Average of the 12 assays before treatment = 0.006 oz/ton or "$ 1.99 /ton."
2. Average of the 12 assays after treatment = 0.017 oz/ton or "$ 5.72 /ton."
3. The Iron King assays were higher and therefore more accurate, as their procedure is to bring each sample "just to dryness," whereas most other laboratories over-dry each sample, unknowingly ensuring that the gold is encapsulated in a hardened acid salt.

Comment:

1. The assays of the untreated samples varied by as much as 1,800%, whereas the assays with much of the acid salts removed varied by only 236%. The average increase in value after removing the acid salts was 287%.
2. The substantial variance in fire assays of the same sample is due to both the acid slag and nugget effects (caused by the occurrence of clusters of encapsulated gold crystals) of the unwashed sample, and probable nugget effect with minor acid slag effect of the sample which has most of the acid salts removed.
3. Iron King labs dried its samples for the least amount of time thereby producing the least precipitation of salts and obtained the highest assays: Loring dried the longest thereby producing the most salt crystallization resulting in the lowest assays.

101

Having discovered that Arizona ores were suffering from acid slag effect, larger samples were tested for recovery by differential charging. Table #3 gives the results of some of these tests.

TABLE #3

Arizona porphyry copper samples processed by the DCRS process

Porphyry Tailings	Sample Size (lbs)	Recovery DCRS oz/ton	Assay Virgin oz/ton	Treated oz/ton	Recovery Mine oz/ton
Miami Magma	100	0.0295	0.010		0.0003
Chino tailings	71	0.0340	0.006	0.061	0.0004
Chino Old Tails	400	0.0242	0.011	0.088	N/A
Chino Old Tails	500	0.0593	0.001	0.075	N/A
Chino Old Tails	354	0.0392	0.014	0.165	N/A
Kidd Creek Canada	55	0.0295	0.010		0.0010

Sulfuric acid in the tailings has caused salt encapsulation of the gold. The DCRS process which uses large volumes of high velocity water is effective at dissolving some of these salts, but not all, liberating some of the gold for recovery.

Porphyry copper engineers calculate the total cost of operating the DCRS system from their tailings line at $0.32 per ton. The amount of salt encapsulated gold recovered potentially could increase the profits of these mines several fold.

With numbers like these and potential like this, surely the copper industry will take notice. Indeed, many have been intrigued by the potential. The former chief chemist of Phelps Dodge, one of the world's largest copper companies, says, "The DCRS process is the best process I have ever seen for the recovery of copper metal in a slurry." Engineers have also been intrigued by the possibility to increase efficiency. Unfortunately, these open-minded professionals can only make recommendations. The decision must be made by the Chief Executive Officer, who requires backing from his technical "experts," who of course, have no expertise in differential charging of metals in a slurry. For them to say "yes" they would have to justify their decision, thereby exposing their ignorance in this field of physics, resulting in the inevitable question, "Why are we paying you?" It is much safer for them to say "no," as then all that they have to say is "It doesn't work," thereby not putting their paychecks in jeopardy. Besides, if they admitted that substantial gold was being lost in processing the copper, that would be the same as saying that the massive tailings, from the ore already processed, also contains substantial gold, which it does. Since these tailing piles were processed by the men who have since risen to the senior ranks, the verification of the gold present would be the same as telling their bosses that they had been inefficient and therefore incompetent. Wow! Why rock the boat? Therefore, the answer by the "experts" to the question of, "Should the copper industry incorporate the DCRS process?" is *"No, No, No !!!"*, even before they look at it.

However, other professionals had expressed interest in the technology, which means the "expert" metallurgist had to get involved in the evaluation. Besides, it was not just a question of verifying assays, which their chief chemist was doing. Their tailings had been run by the truckload, and the engineers had the produced gold *"in their hands."* Besides, the proposal was to install the required equipment for the testing at no cost to the copper industry. What reason could be given for rejecting such a reasonable offer ? Well, as explained before, many people in the industry were benefiting from the status quo, and these people were all in influential positions. One powerful and wealthy investor in the technology suggested that as he was also an investor in the copper industry, he ask the CEO the question at the annual shareholder's meeting, "Why is the company not looking at the DCRS process that could allow the company to triple its' profits ?" Although tempting, it was felt that such a move would put all those engineers and professionals, who were already sympathetic to a DCRS test, on the political hot seat. Thus, the project was pursued through the upper levels of management who expressed their desire to "proceed with the testing." However, the testing would be "subject to approval from the legal department". There was only one condition, and that was that the first project undertaken would have to be done on the first proposal given the company, and that was the testing of the existing rich surface tailings that were currently filling the once pristine lake that existed before the mine started up. The legal decision was simple, and in our opinion correct, and decisive, *"No!"* Environmental groups were threatening multi-billion dollar lawsuits, and any activity would draw their attention to the tailings.

Dismissed, but not deterred, we continued to work with the now converted copper professionals. The company was about to open another massive porphyry copper deposit, and that meant that the historically gold rich surface ore could be recovered inexpensively with the DCRS process. Representative samples of the expensive cores were provided, and turned out to be rich, 0.100 oz/ton (which was typical for this type of deposit), and readily recoverable. Wow! At last success. What could go wrong? Well, the chief chemist coordinating the project retired, and his replacement, highly recommended by the "experts," simply went to the top of a heap leach test pile to provide us with an "unrepresentative" sample which only contained only 0.010 oz/ton, which was easily recovered but only one-tenth of the proven grade. He then summarily dismissed the project as *"uneconomical."*

In another test set up by the "expert" of another major copper company, and in the presence ot their CEO, "absolutely no gold was recovered." As previous testing had recovered economic *gold in hand*, the experts were forced to explain that they had concluded that the gold recovered had come from contamination of the DCRS equipment, and just to prove it, they had provided ore which definitely contained no gold. Then when no gold was recovered, they concluded that the DCRS equipment "must have been clean, but 'may not have been' when the previous tests had been run." With no gold to show the understanding CEO, he left frustrated and disappointed, and the project was another failure.

CHAPTER SIXTEEN

THE GOLDEN SUMMARY

Because of its density, luster, color, malleability, softness, conductivity and last but not least, rarity, gold has been given a special place in both history and the hearts of mankind. From its first discovery it has been cherished and possessed to the point where men will kill for its possession. As a result, it has often been the favorite topic of discussion. This, over the history of mankind, has led to true stories turning into fables of disbelief, such as the goose that laid the golden egg.

The possession of gold was always reserved for royalty only, and they even chose to take it with them into their next life, which was a violation of golden rule #7, *You can't take it with you*. Despite execution if caught, most cultures secretly possessed gold, taking it to their graves. This led to the distasteful practice, that has filled the history of mankind, of grave robbing. By the 1500s, the Spaniards had perfected the art of grave robbing, as they filled their ships with bullion stolen from the graves of Indians in the New World.

As grave robbing opportunities depleted, man turned to developing better technology to recover gold from the rich surface mines. These vast and highly possessed golden treasures changed the basis of values, first in Europe, and then the rest of the world.

It became the real value as the basis for exchange of goods. The men mining the gold gradually displaced royalty as the possessors of the most gold. However, by the end of the 19th century, the rich surface deposits were depleting, and these men, who by now basically owned the world, required a new technology to recover the complexed gold in the massive, deeper deposits. Then, just as the gold industry became desperate for a solution, a jeweler accidentally discovered that gold could readily be dissolved by cyanide. The gold industry converted overnight to the new process, and for the next hundred years, up to the present, there has been no major change in the process used to recover most of the world's gold.

Unfortunately, the proliferation of man has left very few spots in the world where the presumed dangerous cyanide can be used safely. As a result, its use is being gradually curtailed. Today, the industry is almost desperate for a new and safer processs to extract the micron gold from ores. The newly developed differential charge recovery system appears to have all of the required parameters. It is a chemical-free process, it recovers gold in milliseconds and at high rates of production, it is a fraction the size of conventional processes and therefore mobile, it takes one tenth of the time to construct, and most importantly, the costs of construction and operation are a fraction of the costs of conventional processes. The concept of differential charging was so new that *"none"* of the patent claims were challenged, which was a first in the U.S. Patent Office. Therein lies the basic objection to its acceptance by the gold industry. First, its so new that 99.99% of the industry is unaware it exists. Secondly, the "experts," who are asked to assess it, have no expertise with the parameters the DCRS process employs, and therefore will summarily reject it least they show their ignorance to their employers. And lastly, historically major industry has always been reluctant to accept new technology.

So what will be the final outcome? Well, history will repeat itself, and the truth will prevail. This means that in the near future the gold industry will discover that gold can be readily recovered by differential charging. Other metals will also be recovered. For example, mercury, which is uncontrollably lost in conventional processes, is effectively recovered by the DCRS process. This means that the system will be used for environmental cleanups, including other metals such as silver and copper. The only prerequisites are that the element to be recovered has to be metallic, electrically conductive and exposed to receive an electrical charge. Initially experiments have shown that diamonds have also been recovered by the process. The bottom line is that once the DCRS process is discovered, it will proliferate almost instantly all over the world, just as the use of froth floatation did, 40 years after it was patented, one hundred years before.

For those who doubt that something that could have such a major impact on such a huge industry, and for those who do not know of the Montana housewife who discovered froth flotation which also changed the mining industry, I refer you to the book **The Discoverers** by Daniel J. Boorstin (1983, Randon House Inc.). After studying patentable innovation of large corporations in Europe, the United States and Japan, companies such as the Sony Corporation, Intel Corporation, Pilkington Brothers Ltd. and the Honda Corporation, Boorstin concludes that "Large bureaucratic organizations *stifle innovation*," and that "the innovations that do arise, come primarily from entrepreneurs and small business." He writes that "These small groups are undeterred by committees, board approvals, and other bureaucratic delays, allowing the inventor to experiment, test, recycle, and try again with little time lost." He notes that when it comes to funding, "If entrepreneurs are turned down by one source, other sources can be sought in myriads of creative combinations." Sounds like DCRS. Also the financial backers of these entrepreneurs "Recognize that actual outcomes generally depend on subjective factors and not numbers." Large corporations demand the opposite: facts, facts and more objective facts. Boorstin writes that "To manage the inevitable *chaos of innovation* productively, the approvals which cause delays at every turn must be removed, and an atmosphere supportive of innovation must be created." He notes that "Since it takes *a chain of 'yeses' and only one 'no' to kill a project*, management layers have to be all but eliminated and the most successful companies have only small development teams that normally include only six or seven 'key' people." He notes at Sony they say "We have several alternative projects constantly going and before there is a complete loss, we try to *'smell'* (once again subjective thinking) the potential outcome without penalizing the losing teams." Hewlett-Packard states that "Each entrepreneurial startup has a small team, led by a champion in low-cost facilities." Boorstin concludes that "Many of the best concepts and solutions come from projects partly hidden or 'bootlegged' by the organization." Thus, even when the research and development comes from a large corporation, it is made successful using the same keep-it-simple principles as those used in small corporations, such as DCRS, who were also successful researching and developing new technology

   Meanwhile, DCRS is currently pursuing prospects such as gold and diamonds in Venezuela, Panama and South Africa, and numerous gold prospects here in America. This time, however, we have attracted the attention of the top officials in the gold industry, who have a vested interest in the success of the technology. Only when the last chapter in the story of man is written will the last chapter in the story of gold be written. Thus, the last chapter in the story of gold, *If It Glitters*, must remain unwritten, however, stay tuned for the more results as the next chapter in the story of gold is about to begin.

> *But it cost more than it's worth, to dig in the earth,*
> *And tunnel from level to level,*
> *Searching for gold, men quickly turn old,*
> *Most selling their souls to the devil.*
>   *And the story continues . . .*

Hard Rock Gold From Colorado - 3000X

Hard Rock Gold From California - 3000X

Hard Rock Gold From Manitoba - 5000X

Hard Rock Gold From Nevada - 1500X

109

First Gold From DCRS Process, May 1978

First Gold Processing Test Plant, A.C.P., 1978

A.C.P. Gravel Plant, Edmonton, 1978

Bank of 20 Flow Through Electroamalgamator

Small Mobile DCRS at Moab, Utah, 1980

Mongoose #1 at Redding, California, 1981

Mongoose #1 at DCRS Mill, Arizona, 1988

**Scoop of Gold Bullion
With Cup of Nuggets**

Pictorial #2: The "Mongoose" Operating at Various Locations In the United States

Invisible Gold and Mercury From
Dry Nevada Lake Beds

Free Milling Gold, Waste Rock
Redding, California, September 1981

Mongoose At LaSalle Mountain, Utah, July 1982

Concentration of Precious Metals

Mongoose At Gold Gulch, New Mexico, April 1982

Ultra Fine Placer Gold Recovery

Pictorial #2: The "Mongoose" Operating at Various Locations In the United States

Gold Gulch, New Mexico, April 1982

LaSalle Mountain, Utah, July 1982

113

Pictorial #3: The "Mongoose" Operating in the Yukon and One Day's Gold Recovery

Kelsey, Yukon, September 1982

September 11, 1982   Dicore Truck Product

114

Pictorial #4: Small "Autocon" in Operation Demonstrating High Force Mini Swirls

#1 HFMS System as Water Starts With Trays and Cells Visible

#2 HFMS With water at High Velocity, Entrapped Air Visible

#3 HFMS System as Ore Starts to be Added to Water, Air Visible

#4 HFMS System with Turbulent Slurry at 10% Solids by Weight

Pictorial #5: Production "Dual Stacked Autocon" Mounted in Container